FIELD GUIDE

to

WILDLIFE

of

THE GAMBIA

AN INTRODUCTION TO COMMON FLOWERS & ANIMALS

(554 COLOUR PHOTOGRAPHS)

by Dr David Penney

This book is available directly from the publisher at:
www.siriscientificpress.co.uk

ISBN 978-0-9558636-1-5

Published by Siri Scientific Press, Manchester, UK

This book was designed, written, type set and published entirely within the UK by the author and Siri Scientific Press.

Cover design by Barry Burke, Manchester, UK, © 2009, Siri Scientific Press.

The author can be contacted by email at david.penney@manchester.ac.uk or African. Nephila@hotmail.co.uk (please try the former address first and put Gambian field guide in the subject field).

Contents

This book is dedicated to

ALL THOSE INVOLVED IN THE CONSERVATION AND PROTECTION OF WILDLIFE AND NATURAL HABITATS WITHIN THE GAMBIA

INTRODUCTION & SCOPE

The Gambia is located on the Atlantic coast of tropical West Africa between latitudes 13 and 14 degrees north, with an open coastline of 70 km and is otherwise surrounded by Senegal for its entire land border of 740 km. There is a sheltered coastline of 200 km along the River Gambia dominated by extensive mangrove systems and mudflats. The Gambia loosely tracks the course of the river as it meanders inland (the river originates in Guinea and flows from east to west) and with an area of only 11,295 km^2 (10,000 km^2 of dry land) is the smallest country on the continent. In contrast to many other West African countries it is relatively flat, with the highest point less than 100 m above sea level. The country is situated on the Continental Terminal, a vast Tertiary sandstone plateau, which originated from the iron-rich soils to the east. These were eroded from the continent into the Atlantic and then over millions of years re-deposited against the coastline and lithified (turned to stone).

The sub-tropical climate is pleasant, with two distinct seasons determined by the imbalance at the boundary of the high-pressure regions north and south of the equator (the ITCZ: inter-tropical convergence zone). Generally speaking, November to June consist of dry savannah winds (Harmattan), whereas from July to October the country sees heavy downpours and is lusciously green. Even in the height of the rainy season it does not rain every day and much of the rainfall occurs overnight. There are still many days of uninterrupted sunshine, but the high humidity can be rather oppressive. However, Gambian biodiversity is at its most spectacular during the rainy season, not least because the rains initiate an explosion of a great diversity of flowering plants and a visit at this time of year is highly recommended.

The population of the country is nearly 1.7 million, increasing annually with a growth rate of approximately 2.8%. Given that the major economic activities within The Gambia, such as agriculture, agro-processing, fisheries, livestock production and tourism have quite specific land usage requirements, the increasing population size and the subsequent increase in demand for these products will undoubtedly affect the relative abundance and distribution of the various habitat types present in the country. What the knock on effects of this will be for Gambian wildlife is unclear.

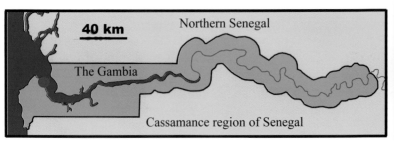

40 km

Northern Senegal

The Gambia

Cassamance region of Senegal

The Gambia and other tropical West African countries: **1**, Mauritania; **2**, Senegal; **3**, Mali; **4**, Niger; **5, The Gambia**; **6**, Guinea-Bissau; **7**, Guinea; **8**, Burkina Faso; **9**, Benin; **10**, Nigeria; **11**, Cameroon; **12**, Sierra Leone; **13**, Liberia; **14**, Ivory Coast; **15**, Ghana; **16**, Togo; **17**, Equatorial Guinea; **18**, Gabon. Red dot in bottom figure represents Banjul, the capital of The Gambia.

The Gambia lies within the transition zone at the interface of relatively moist Guinean forest–savannah mosaic in the south and the drier Sudanian woodlands in the north. Within this system, the country supports many diverse habitat types including marine and coastal, estuary and mangroves, banto faros (barren hypersaline flats derived from the mangroves), brackish and freshwater river banks, swamp forest, freshwater swamps and other wetlands (e.g., bolons, rice fields, ponds, etc.; obviously more prominent in the rainy season), forest (primary coastal e.g., Bijilo, primary gallery e.g., Abuko, secondary e.g., Tanji, etc.) and woodland, forest–savannah mosaic, villages, farmland and fallow land. Urban environments and especially hotel gardens should not be underestimated as sites for seeing interesting birds and insects, particularly as many of them have well maintained flower beds throughout the year.

Such a diverse range of habitat types can be expected to contain a high biodiversity of indigenous plants and animals, in addition to naturalized introductions and migrant species. This is certainly the case, but our knowledge of the fauna and flora is far from complete and differs significantly for different groups. In general, those groups that are useful (e.g., for building materials, have medicinal properties, are edible, are dangerous to humans or their crops) tend to be better known than less useful groups. Probably the best known group is birds (which don't really fit easily in any of the above categories). This is because of the hard work of Clive Barlow and colleagues, which resulted in an excellent, user-friendly guidebook to all birds of the Senegambia region. For this reason very few birds are included in this volume.

Other vertebrates, such as mammals, reptiles and amphibians are also well known. Plants are relatively well studied, but given their high biodiversity much still remains to be done before we have a full picture of the country's flora. Invertebrates, such as insects (with the exception of butterflies and dragonflies), arachnids (spiders, scorpions, etc.) and myriapods (millipedes and centipedes) are probably the most poorly studied and hence form the main focus of this book, which is restricted primarily to terrestrial species.

The correct identification of many invertebrate species requires detailed microscopic examination by relevant experts, which may not be available for some groups. Hence, you will notice varying degrees of taxonomic resolution. Many of the species illustrated are first records for The Gambia and some may even be new to science.

Coastal sands with salt tolerant sand-binding plants; scrub & lagoon systems

Rice fields with African oil palms at the end of the dry season

Freshwater pond, excellent habitat for wading birds, dragonflies & water lilies

Mangrove habitat system, good for wading birds, fiddler crabs & mudskippers

Rhun palm dominated primary coastal forest, with coastal scrub in the foreground

Secondary coastal forest has a very different structure, note the lack of rhun palms

FLOWERING PLANTS

One cannot fail to be amazed at the diversity and beauty of flowering plants in The Gambia, regardless of the time of year, although they are at their most spectacular during the rainy season. More than 1,000 plant species (including trees, shrubs, climbers, herbs and grasses) have been recorded. Some flower for most of the year, whereas others are visible for only very brief periods. Many trees flower during the dry season, whereas many of the herbaceous species appear during the rains. Some species have flowers that open only during the morning or that are wilted by midday, whereas others flower at night and are pollinated by bats (e.g., the baobab tree) or moths (some of the crinum lilies).

No true tropical rainforest exists in The Gambia, but species-rich groundwater-fed forests can be found in Abuko, Pirang and Bijilo. Bijilo Forest is particularly interesting because it also includes a large element of coastal scrubland and exposed clearings in several places, both with their own distinctive floras.

Roadside verges, wasteland and harvested rice fields during the dry season are all good places to look for interesting flowers, although many of these are considered as weed species. Many flowering plants are grown as ornamentals and it is worth keeping an eye out for unusual species for sale by the multiple vendors along the main highways.

Many plants are grown as foodstuffs or are utilized for various other purposes, such as building materials, firewood, making twine, producing refreshing herbal drinks, and one with a very pungent odor is used to deter mosquitoes. A large number of plants are also used locally for their medicinal properties, although different people use the same plant for different purposes and others use different plants for the same purpose. It is commonplace to see trees stripped of patches of bark or local Gambians picking leaves, either for their own use of for sale in some of the markets.

Many of the species illustrated are showy and difficult to miss, but others will require a keen eye to spot, either because they are small or because they grow as individuals. In addition to indigenous species, many introduced or pantropical plants are also prevalent. Previous rough estimates suggested more than 1,600 flowering plant species exist in The Gambia, but little is known about their biology or distribution, so new species records should not be unexpected.

Egyptian lotus *Nymphaea lotus* (family Nymphaeaceae, water lily having large leaves with sharp serrations)

Water lily *Nymphaea micrantha* (family Nymphaeaceae, leaves rounded, without sharp serrations)

Nymphoides indica (family Menyanthaceae, pond fringes; although it resembles a water lily it is actually a herb, pantropical)

Sora *Leptadenia hastata* (family Asclepiadaceae, twining climber used widely in local medicine)

Broad-leaved ground orchid *Eulophia guineensis* (family Orchidaceae, in shade)

Neem *Azadirachta indica* (family Meliaceae, leaves contain a powerful insecticide)

Baobab *Adansonia digitata* (family Bombacaceae, huge tree, flowers at night, bat pollinated, all parts used for something)

Guinea peach *Sarcocephalus latifolius* (family Rubiaceae, weaver ants build their nests around developing flowers)

Tridax procumbens (family Asteraceae, wasteland & building sites, a pantropical weed introduced from Central America)

Queensland hemp *Sida rhombifolia* (family Malvaceae, a variable short woody herb, common along roadsides)

Ink plant *Eclipta prostata* (family Compositae, a pantropical weed)

Sida linifolia (family Malvaceae, a widespread weed of crops & in open areas)

Spider lily *Hymenocallis littoralis*
(family Amaryllidaceae, introduced from
tropical America & grown as an ornamental)

Gingerbread plum *Neocarya macrophylla*
(family Chrysobalanaceae, common in
coastal scrub & dry savanna, fruits warty)

Arrowroot lily *Tacca leontopetaloides*
(family Taccaceae, stands conspicuously
proud of close plants in shade-free thickets)

Bani-yitinyero *Macrosphyra longistyla*
(family Rubiaceae, stigma on long style,
produces sticky, orange fluid when receptive)

Crinum lily *Crinum zeylanicum* (family
Amaryllidaceae, moth pollinated at night)

Hoslundia opposita (family Labiatae, forest
edges, highly attractive to butterflies)

Spermacoce verticillata (family Rubiaceae, erect herb common in cultivated crops & damp wasteland)

Monkey grass *Philoxerus vermicularis* (family Amaranthaceae, a sand-binding short, fleshy herb of the upper shore region)

Anthostema senegalense (family Euphorbiaceae, leaves grow downwards, giving a characteristic drooping appearance)

Black mangrove *Avicennia germinans* (family Avicenniaceae, leaves often speckled with salt crystals, exposed pneumatophores)

Button grass *Mitracarpus hirtus* (family Rubiaceae, weed of culitvation/wasteland)

False yam *Icacina oliviformis* (family Icacinaceae, early colonizer of fallow land)

Gambian tea bush *Lippia chevalieri* (family Verbenaceae, erect shrub, dried leaves used to make aromatic, herbal tea)

Mango tree *Mangifera indica* (family Anacardiaceae, common in compounds as a shade tree, delicious fruits in rainy season)

Confetti tree *Maytenus senegalensis* (family Celestraceae, shrub or small tree with leaves & flowers located on stem spines)

Chinese date *Ziziphus mauritiana* (family Rhamnaceae, shrub or small tree, parallel leaf veins distinctive, produces edible fruits)

Ipomoea eriocarpa (family Convolvulaceae, a slender climbing herb)

Winter thorn *Faidherbia albida* (family Leguminosae, savanna tree up to 25 m tall)

Ritchiea capparoides (family Capparaceae, large shrub or tree of Guinean forest zone, found in Abuko Forest but not in Bijilo)

Crocodile's tooth *Capparis tomentosa* (family Capparaceae, thorny savanna shrub or small tree, flower wilted by midday)

Hemp-leaved hibiscus *Hibiscus cannabinus* (family Malvaceae, widespread erect herb with variable leaf shape)

Red sorrel *Hibiscus sabdariffa* (family Malvaceae, leaves used to make green sauce & calyces used to make a red juice drink)

Hibiscus physaloides (family Malvaceae, woody herb, flowers upto 8 cm in diameter)

Kunakalo *Clerodendron capitatum* (family Labiatae, shrub of savanna & closed forest)

Pergularia daemia (family Asclepiadaceae, herbaceous climber, forest edges & coastal scrub, fruit resembles upturned moustache)

Ceylon leadwort *Plumbago zeylanica* (family Plumbaginaceae, coastal scrub, note calyx with characteristic gland hairs)

Merremia tridentata (family Convolvulaceae, two lobes at base of narrow leaves, each with three teeth)

Madagascar periwinkle *Catharanthus roseus* (family Apocynaceae, ornamental introduced from tropical America, also pink)

Merremia aegyptia (family Convolvulaceae, long-stalked leaves with five leaflets)

Wild beniseed *Sesamum radiatum* (family Pedaliaceae, moist, open areas)

Kaba *Saba senegalensis* (family Apocynaceae, forest & forest fringe liane, edible ovoid fruits sold in local markets)

Scrub ipomoea *Ipomoea stolonifera* (family Convolvulaceae, sparsely distributed in exposed coastal scrub)

Yellow oleander *Cascabela thevetia* (family Apocynaceae, ornamental shrub in urban areas, introduced from tropical America)

Black bembo *Lannea acida* (family Anacardiaceae, small tree with yellow finger-like flower spikes at branch tips)

Mexican poppy *Argemome ochroleuca* (family Papaveraceae, wasteland/roadsides)

Grangea maderaspatana (family Compositae, weed of lowland rice fields)

Long-fruited jute *Corchorus olitorius* (family Tiliaceae, leaves with 2 long, thin basal projections, arable & wasteland)

Sickle senna *Senna obtusifolia* (family Leguminosae, fallow & wasteland, young leaves used for making soup)

Ludwigia octovalvis (family Onagraceae, erect, branched herb in damp & flooded areas, a serious weed in rice fields)

Gumbar tree *Gmelina arborea* (family Labiatae, flowers pollinated by sunbirds & eaten by monkeys, introduced from Asia)

Burweed *Triumfetta rhomboidea* (family, Tiliaceae, wasteland & disturbed soils)

Waltheria indica (family Sterculiaceae, chewed by locals & used to clean teeth)

Loofah gourd *Luffa cylindrica* (family
Cucurbitaceae, herbaceous trailer, often in
urban areas, dried fruits used for washing)

West African laburnum *Cassia sieberiana*
(family Leguminosae, a common small tree
species, often put in compounds for shade)

River bean *Sesbania pachycarpa* (family
Leguminosae, a tall shrubby herb
conspicuous in coastal areas)

Rattle box *Crotalaria retusa* (family
Leguminosae, coastal vegetation &
wasteland, probably introduced from Asia)

Sclerocarpus africanus (family Compositae,
wasteland & forest clearings, rainy season)

Aspilia africana (family Compositae, a
highly variable & widespread plant)

Butterfly pea *Clitoria ternatea* (family Leguminosae, herbaceous vine, flowers occasionally white, naturalized ornamental)

Musu-kaffo-jio *Commelina benghalensis* (family Commelinaceae, short herb & a problematic weed in groundnut crops)

Bush tea bush *Hyptis suaveolens* (family Labiatae, pungent herb, the crushed leaves are used as mosquito repellent)

Sphaeranthus senegalensis (family Compositae, a weed of lowland rice fields, often found in association with *Grangea*)

Star thistle *Centaurea perrottetii* (family Compositae, coastal scrub at beach margin)

Goat weed *Ageratum conyzoides* (family Compositae, pantropical herb)

Kunjunborong *Newbouldia laevis* (family Bignoniaceae, a small tree species used for live fencing, with long, cylindrical fruits)

West African mistletoe *Tapinanthus globiferus* (family Loranthaceae, a bushy parasite of various tree species, widespread)

Rice farm grass *Nelsonia canescens* (family Acanthaceae, mat-forming weed of damp, shaded areas including rice fields)

Little girl's cloth *Kohautia grandiflora* (family Rubiaceae, short erect herb & a weed species in cultivated areas)

Ninsi-kumbalingo *Justicia schimperi* (family Acanthaceae, widespread herb)

Asystasia gangetica (family Acanthaceae, widespread in tropical regions)

Papaya *Carica papaya* (family Caricaceae, common in compounds as a source of large, juicy fruits, tropical American introduction)

Sodom apple *Calotropis procera* (family Asclepiadaceae, shrub or small tree, has various medical uses, introduced from Asia)

Ipomoea setifera (family Convolvulaceae, naturalized climbing twiner introduced from tropical America, common along roadsides)

Beach morning glory *Ipomoea pes-capre* (family Convolvulaceae, long, trailing vine, dense growth stalbilizes coastal sand)

Ipomoea triloba (family Convolvulaceae, introduced species from tropical America)

Blue trumpet vine *Thunbergia grandiflora* (family Acanthaceae, common ornamental)

Camel's foot tree *Bauhinia monandra* (family Leguminosae, leaves shaped like a camel's hoof print, introduced from Myanmar)

Frangipani *Plumeria alba* (family Apocynaceae, also with white flowers, often on leafless trees, ornamental in urban areas)

Oleander *Nerium oleander* (Apocynaceae, tall ornamental bush, introduced from the Mediterranean, flowers sometimes white)

Bourgainvillaea *Bourgainvillaea spectabilis* (family Nyctaginaceae common ornamental in urban areas, introduced from S America)

Congo jute *Urena lobata* (family Malvaceae, outer layer of fibrous stem used for rope)

Butterfly bush *Lantana camara* (family Verbenaceae, there is also a red variety)

Seaside purslane *Sesuvium portulacastrum* (family Aizoaceae, succulent herb of littoral zone, sand dunes and edges of salt lagoons)

Monkey's shuttle *Strophanthus sarmentosus* (family Apocynaceae, dry forest & savanna thickets, in flower from mid dry season)

Seaside sword bean *Canavalia rosea* (family Leguminoseae, flowers on spike with drooping tip, common along the coast)

Bell-flowered mimosa *Dichrostachys cinerea* (family Leguminosae, shrub/small tree, leaves chewed to alleviate tooth ache)

Naka burayo *Desmodium velutinum* (family Leguminoseae, savanna woodland)

Tephrosia purpurea (family Leguminoseae, common by roadsides and in dry wasteland)

Red-flowered silk cotton tree *Bombax costatum* (family Bombaceae, young tree with spiny bark, in flower mid dry season)

Flamboyante tree *Delonix regia* (family Leguminosae, common ornamental, flowers from June, introduced from Madagascar)

African locust bean tree *Parkia biglobosa* (family Leguminosae, flower hangs from a long stalk, often seen in cleared arable land)

Flame lily *Gloriosa superba* (family, Colchicaceae, semi-woody herb, flowers change from yellow to red with age)

African tulip tree *Spathodea campanulata* (family Bignoniaceae, common ornamental)

Pride of Barbados *Caesalpinia pulcherrima* (family Leguminosae, common ornamental)

Burning bush *Combretum paniculatum*
(family Combretaceae, climbing shrub in
flower mid dry season, scrub & forest edge)

Butterfly bush or wild sage *Lantana camara*
(family Verbenaceae, there is also a pink &
white variety, highly attractive to butterflies)

Ruspolia hypocrateriformis (family
Acanthaceae, common shrubby plant in
coastal forest throughout the rainy season)

Fireball lily *Scadoxus multiflorus* (family
Amaryllidaceae, short herbaceous plant
conspicuous just before the rainy season)

Crown of thorns *Euphorbia milii* (family
Euphorbiaceae, from Madagascar)

Coral tree *Erythrina senegalensis*
(family Leguminosae, small savanna tree)

FUNGI

Although not strictly part of the flora or fauna (fungi belong in a different biological kingdom), I felt it would be remiss of me to exclude them from this field guide. In addition to their beauty, they are extremely important organisms ecologically, because they break down dead organic matter and so manage the recycling process of nutrients within an ecosystem. Some fungi cause disease in plants and animals (e.g., athletes foot and ringworm), some produce medicine (e.g., penicillin) and others form important foodstuffs (e.g., mushrooms). Gambian fungi tend to be more readily visible during the wet season. Little is known about West African fungal diversity, so many of the following identifications must be considered tentative.

Auricularia sp. (usually found on dead trunks, rarely on live trees; tiny 'insects' on the underside are springtails = Collembola)

Rhodotus sp. (Basidiomycota, Aphyllophorales, specifically associated with palms)

Trametes leonina
(Basidiomycota, Aphyllophorales)

Crinipellis sp.
(Basidiomycota, Agaricales)

Agaricus sp. (young specimens have white coloured gills that turn pink and then dark with age; this is a large species)

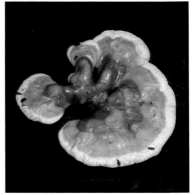

Ganoderma lucidum (Basidiomycota, Aphyllophorales, a parasitic fungus, commonly on living roots or trunks)

Meriliopsis sp. (Basidiomycota, Aphyllophorales, fresh material saturated with water)

Leucocoprinus sp. (usually found on termite mounds and a much favoured food of slugs, note the specimen in the top right of photo)

Possibly *Phellinus* sp. (Basidiomycota, Aphyllophorales)

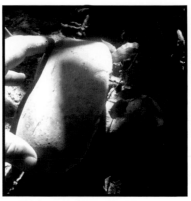

Phlebopus sudanicus (Basidiomycota, Agaricales, an ectomycorrhizal fungus)

Hexagonia sp. (Basidiomycota, Aphyllophorales, on dead trunks or bark)

Hexagonia hirta (Basidiomycota, Aphyllophorales, usually on dead trunks)

Hexagonia tenuis (Basidiomycota, Aphyllophorales, usually on dead trunks)

Dacryopinax spathularia (Ascomycota, usually on dead trunks)

Hypoxylon sp. (Basidiomycota, Aphyllophorales, on dead trunks or bark)

Marasmius confertus (Basidiomycota, Agaricales)

Mammals & Birds

More than 100 species of mammals (excluding domestic species) are currently known to occur in The Gambia. Bats form the most speciose group, with at least 30 species recorded. The large frugivorous fruit bats are difficult to miss as they fly overhead at dusk. Smaller insect-eating bats can also be seen flitting around rapidly at the same time of day, performing quite amazing aerial acrobatics as they locate insects in flight using their incredibly sensitive sonar capabilities.

The vast majority of the remaining mammal species consist of rodents, carnivores and ungulates in similar proportions. Primates, aquatic mammals (whales, dolphins, seals and manatees) and oddities such as the aardvark make up the rest.

Many mammals are nocturnal or extremely secretive and so are difficult to spot. However, if you are in the right place at the right time you should have no problems seeing the four main primate species. The tiny bushbaby is both nocturnal and secretive, spending much of its time up in the canopy, but you may be lucky and get a glimpse of one or several if out and about at night with a torch. Bijilo Forest is a good place to see the endangered western red colobus monkey and the callithrix monkey. Kiang West National Park is a good location for baboons and patas monkeys. Sometimes captive specimens of the last two species and hyaenas can be seen at Abuko Nature Reserve, which is also a good place to see bushbuck drinking from the pool.

Rodents, such as Gambian sun squirrels and striped ground squirrels are active during the day and are often seen up in the trees and down on the ground respectively. Porcupines are nocturnal and seldom seen, however, their presence is belied by the occasional shed quill found along a nature trail. These are used by local women to braid hair. Mongooses are another mammal you may be likely to encounter during the daytime, if you happen to be in the right place at the right time. Unfortunately, nocturnal carnivores such as civets and genets are more often seen as road kills than they are as living individuals going about their business.

Several species including lions, giraffes and the African elephant inhabited The Gambia in the past but are now locally extinct. However, several large species, such as leopards, hyaenas and hippopotamuses still occur, albeit in smaller numbers than they once did. Unfortunately, little information is available regarding the current status of many of these species, so it is difficult to determine whether or not more of those species that remain are under threat of extinction within The Gambia.

The Gambia is famed for its bird biodiversity, which boasts more than 540 species and is well documented, primarily through the user-friendly field guide produced by Clive Barlow and colleagues. For this reason only a handful of birds are included here.

DON'T FEED THE MONKEYS!

These are wild animals and they have all the food they need in their natural environment. Feeding them increases your risk of catching fatal diseases, such as rabies and herpes B virus, both of which are incurable and inevitably end in a slow, painful death! It makes them bold and aggressive towards humans, so they may attack and seriously injure those sensible people (including young children) who do not offer them food. Such supplementary feeding increases the size of the primate populations beyond the carrying capacity of the forests and encourages them to leave their natural habitat and enter hotels and homes in search of food, especially out of the tourist season. Such behaviour may result in them being killed on the road by cars or harmed by people if they become serious pests. By feeding them you are endangering them, yourself and others.

It is irresponsible, irrational and dangerous behaviour!

Crested porcupine *Hystrix cristata* (family Hystricidae, the largest rodent in Africa, raises and vibrates quills when alarmed)

Gambian sun squirrel *Heliosciurus gambianus* (family Sciuridae, in trees; ground squirrels *Xerus* have lateral stripes)*

Callithrix (or green) monkey *Chlorocebus sabaeus* (family Cercopithecidae, the most easily seen Gambian primate)

Western red colobus *Piliocolobus badius temminckii* (family Colobidae, endangered = liable to be extinct within one generation!)

Patas monkey *Erythrocebus patas* (family Cercopithecidae, the fastest known primate)

Western baboon *Papio papio* (family Cercopithecidae, more common inland)

Spotted hyaena *Crocuta crocuta* (family Hyaenidae, savanna, rarely in dense forest, stiped hyaena also found in The Gambia)

Western bushbuck *Traegelaphus scriptus scriptus* (family Bovidae, forest thickets & dense bush, usually close to water)

Red-billed hornbill *Tockus erythrorhynchus* (family Bucerotidae, usually seen in pairs, sexes similar, male has slightly larger bill)

African grey hornbill *Tockus nasutus* (family Bucerotidae, prefers open savanna with tall trees, a common breeding resident)

Abyssinian roller *Coracias abyssinica*[+] (family Coraciidae, common)

Little bee-eater *Merops pusillus* (family Meropidae, nests in earth banks)

Beautiful sunbird *Nectarinia pulchella** (family Nectariniidae, female drab, male metallic green/red/yellow with long tail)

Senegal coucal *Centropus senegalensis** (family Cuculidae, a medium-sized bird with sexes alike, common year round)

Red-billed firefinch *Lagonosticta senegala** (family Estrildidae, small bird, common in groups on ground around human habitation)

Yellow-crowned gonolek *Laniarius barbarus** (family Malaconotidae, usually in pairs in dense bush, sexes similar)

Blue-breasted kingfisher *Halcyon malimbica* (family Alcedinidae, mangroves & forests)*

Palm-nut vulture *Gypohierax angolensis** (family Accipitridae, sexes alike)

Reptiles & Amphibians

The Gambia has a diverse herptofauna, although newts and salamanders are absent. Toads are common, but usually hide during the heat of the day. Bullfrogs, reed and tree frogs are diverse but are more often heard rather than seen. There are more than 40 species of snakes, including several venomous (e.g., cobras, mambas and puff adders) and non-venomous (e.g., pythons and bush snakes) types. Of the nine dangerous snake species found in The Gambia only two species of cobra and the puff adder are relatively common. If you are scared of snakes do not worry, most of the time they sense you coming and disappear long before you approach them. Short stay visitors are unlikely to see one in the wild. Nonetheless, you should remain alert for them when out and about in the bush.

Most of the reptiles you are likely to encounter will be lizards, particularly the agamas and skinks (both brown and orange-flanked). During their breeding season male agamas have bright yellow heads and blue/black tails; the females have orange patches on their flanks. Armitage's skink has only ever been found in The Gambia, but it will almost certainly occur in the coastal regions of Senegal and possibly elsewhere. Their limbs are minute and rudimentary; but they seem to 'swim' through the sand with great ease and speed. Nile monitors are the largest lizards in Africa, but like snakes they will usually hear you coming and disappear into the bush. However, in some places they have become accustomed to humans and do not dash off as readily. These lizards are voracious predators and will eat anything they can catch. They have powerful limbs with strong claws and often dig in the ground in search of eggs, leaving telltale excavations in their wake. Another large lizard is Bosc's monitor, although these are much more sluggish than the former species. There are small, swift-moving tree geckos, in addition to the larger species more familiar around human habitations. If you are really lucky you might even see a chameleon, famed for their camouflage, their extremely long tongue and their ability to move their eyes independently of one another.

Historically, three species of crocodile occurred in The Gambia (slender-snouted *Mecistops cataphractus*, West African dwarf *Osteolaemus tetraspis tetraspis* and West African *Crocodylus suchus*, formerly considered to be the Nile crocodile). Their current status is unclear and the first two species are certainly endangered and locally extinct in many places. However, a new conservation initiative by Crocos Ark Trust aims to captive breed these species at the Gambian reptiles farm and reintroduce the offspring in appropriate habitats in the future. It is usually possible to see wild crocodiles in the pool at Abuko nature reserve and you can get up close and personal with them at the sacred crocodile pool at Katchikally.

Several species of large, marine chelonians (e.g., hawksbill, olive-ridley, loggerhead, leatherback and green turtles) occur in the coastal waters, but not all are known to breed on Gambian beaches. Freshwater and terrestrial species include tortoises, soft-shelled turtles, terrapins and mud turtles. An excellent place to see many different reptile species and to learn about their biology and conservation is the Gambian reptiles farm just past Gunjur.

West African reed frog *Hyperolius nitidulus* (family Hyperoliidae)

Common African toad *Bufo regularis* (family Bufonidae, very common in many habitats, especially in the rainy season)

West African crocodile *Crocodylus suchus*[+] (family Crocodylidae)

Bell's back hinged tortoise *Kinixys belliana nogueyi* (family Testudinidae)

Orange-flanked skink *Mabuya perrotetii*
(family Scincidae, the largest Gambian
skink, active mainly in the rainy season)

Brown-flanked skink *Mabuya affinis*
(family Scincidae, small, common and very
fast, often seen foraging in forest leaf litter)

Armitage's skink *Chalcides armitagei*
(family Scincidae, only recorded from The
Gambia, they 'swim' rapidly through sand)

Bosc's monitor *Varanus exanthematicus*
(family Varanidae, a large, sluggish lizard of
grassland and open woodlands)

Adult nile monitor *Varanus niloticus*[+]
(family Varanidae, large, fast & aggessive)

Juvenile nile monitor *Varanus niloticus*
(family Varanidae, common in forests)

Brook's house gecko *Hemidactylus brooki angulatus* (family Gekkonidae, nocturnal, often seen foraging around lights)

Diurnal dwarf gecko *Lygodactylus gutturalis* (family Gekkonidae, small and extremely fast tree-dwelling species)[+]

Agama lizard *Agama agama* (Agamidae, drab dry season form, the most common Gambian lizard, found in most habitats)

Agama lizard *Agama agama* (Agamidae, breeding male has blue body & yellow head, female has orange patches on flanks)

Chameleon *Chamaeleo senegalensis* (family Chamaeleonidae)

Worm lizard *Cynisca feae* (family Amphisbaenidae, harmless)

Common bush snake *Philothamnus irregularis* (family Colubridae, harmless, but often mistaken for a green mamba)

Herald snake *Crotaphopeltis hotamboeia* (family Colubridae, common & widespread back-fanged snake of moist areas)

Egg-eating snake *Dasypeltis scabra* (family Colubridae, eats whole eggs, then regurgitates the shell, forest & savanna)

Slender African beauty snake *Psammophis elegans* (family Colubridae, back-fanged, probably the most common Gambian snake)

Olive sand snake *Psammophis phillipsi* (family Colubridae, back-fanged)

Wolf snake *Lycophidion albomaculatum* (family Colubridae, harmless)

House snake *Lamprophis lineatus* (family Colubridae, docile & harmless, enters houses & stores to feed on mice, etc.)

Royal python *Python regius* around my mother's neck! (family Boidae, harmless, usually docile, open forests & grasslands)

Ground cobra or garter snake *Elapsoidea semiannulata moebiusi*[+] (family Elapidae, poisonous, short snake, savanna woodland)

Night adder *Causus rhombeatus* (Viperidae, poisonous, common in compounds where it feeds on toads, easily trodden on at night!)

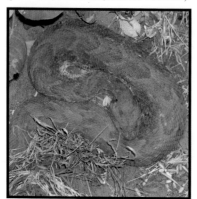

Puff adder *Bitis arietans arietans* (family Viperidae, very dangerous)

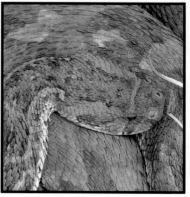

Close up of puff adder head[+] (these snakes have large fangs and very potent venom)

INSECTS

Insects differ from other animals in having their mouthparts located outside their mouth, they have three distinct body parts (head, thorax and abdomen), six pairs of jointed walking legs and usually (but not always) two pairs of wings. As in any tropical terrestrial ecosystem, insects are the most biodiverse group to be found in The Gambia. Some estimates predict three million insect species to be present in tropical Africa, but how many of these occur within The Gambia is unclear because little information is available for groups other than butterflies and dragonflies. Many of the species illustrated in the following pages are new records for the Gambian fauna.

Despite this lack of entomological knowledge, Gambians appreciate that insects are of the utmost importance for several reasons. Many are medically important as vectors of disease. Mosquitoes spread malaria, dengue fever, yellow fever and the filarial worm that causes elephantiasis. Sleeping sickness is carried by tsetse flies, river blindness by tiny blackflies and sand flies are responsible for leishmaniasis. Fleas and lice can also spread unpleasant (and sometimes fatal) illnesses.

Insects are also important as pests of agriculture, including livestock. Some estimates suggest that more than ten percent of world crop produce is lost to insects annually and here in The Gambia locust swarms can have devastating consequences in this respect. Some cockroaches, beetles and moths infest and contaminate stored foods. Termites and wood-boring beetles eat away at wooden structures and can destroy whole buildings. Some insects have painful stings.

However, it is not all doom and gloom. It is less than one percent of insect species that cause problems for humans, with many of the remainder being extremely beneficial. They pollinate flowering plants, upon which we are dependent for food and oxygen. Many are predators or parasites of non-beneficial insects and thus help keep their populations in check. Honey (produced in The Gambia) would be non-existent without bees. Some insects are edible (e.g., beetle larvae, termites, locusts, some caterpillars, bee larvae and even dragonflies) although this practice known as entomophagy is not as common in The Gambia as in many other West African countries.

Finally, many insects are creatures of great beauty and can be studied with relative ease (and at little or no expense) in just about any location you may find yourself at within The Gambia.

Dragonflies and damselflies (order Odonata) are particularly prevalent at certain times of the year, especially during the wet season because their larvae are aquatic. They are voracious predators as both larvae and adults. Dragonflies (suborder: Anisoptera) are larger, heavier, stronger fliers than the damselflies (suborder: Zygoptera). When resting, dragonflies sit with their wings widespread or angled forwards and downwards, whereas damselflies rest with their wings folded above them, along the length of the body.

Despite many common misconceptions dragonflies do not sting or bite and are totally harmless. On the contrary, they are highly beneficial to humans because each individual eats a great many small insects, especially mosquitoes. Odonata are visual hunters, catching their prey on the wing using their bristly legs as a basket trap. They require excellent eyesight and their compound eyes are extremely large. Each one may contain up to 30,000 individual lenses or omatidia. Odonata also mate during flight and it is not unusual to see copulating pairs in their unique, tandem wheel formation with the male clasping the female by her head. At least 75 species have been recorded from The Gambia. You are more likely to see them in more exposed areas rather than in dense forest.

In some parts of West Africa (e.g., Nigeria) locals have been known to eat dragonflies during times of famine, but I have been informed that this practice does not occur in The Gambia. Non-entomologists may confuse antlions and ascalaphids (order Neuroptera–see later) for Odonata. However, the two can be easily separated by the former having long, clubbed antennae, whereas the antennae are short and bristle-like in dragonflies.

Damselfly *Ceriagron glabrum* at rest
(family Coenagrionidae, male)

Tiny swamp bluet *Azuragrion vansomereni*
(family Coenagrionidae)

Widow dragonfly *Palpopleura portia* at rest (family Libellulidae, male, usually seen resting on grass, often in large numbers)

Widow dragonfly *Palpopleura portia* at rest (family Libellulidae, female – impossible to differentiate from *P. lucia* without disection)

Black percher dragonfly *Diplacodes lefebvrei* (family Libellulidae, female, male with a much darker body)

Dragonfly *Pantala flavescens* at rest (family Libellulidae, male, very common, often seen in gardens)

Red basker dragonfly *Crocothemis erythraea* (family Libellulidae, male)

Long skimmer *Orthetrum trinacria* (family Libellulidae, eating a pierid butterfly)

Strong skimmer *Orthetrum brachiale* (family Libellulidae, male at rest in typical pose with wings forwards & downwards)

Strong skimmer *Orthetrum brachiale* at rest (family Libellulidae, female, common & widespread in various habitats)

Banded groundling *Brachythemis leucosticta* (family Libellulidae, male, low fliers, often settling on the ground)

Banded groundling *Brachythemis leucosticta*** (family Libellulidae, female, gregarious, common on mud/bare ground)

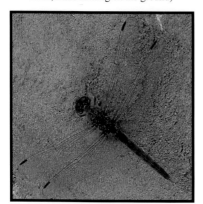

Common wall dragonfly *Bradinopyga strachani*[+] (family Libellulidae, male)

Common wall dragonfly *Bradinopyga strachani* (family Libellulidae, female)

Cockroaches (order Blattodea) are common in The Gambia, especially as pests in domestic situations, as is the case the world over. However, there are also many non-pest species, particularly in the forests. They are nocturnal and most are broadly oval, flattened, have long antennae and are extremely fast runners. They have biting mouthparts and feed mainly on vegetable matter. In most cases, they are small and inconspicuous animals that live within the leaf litter. However, some species are larger, making them somewhat more conspicuous. Females deposit their eggs in an egg case (or ootheca). In some species this is carried around, projecting from the back of the abdomen. Of the specimens illustrated, *Rhyparobia* is large and a highly sought after prey item by emerald cockroach wasps *Ampulex compressa*. The remainder are medium-sized (up to 25 mm).

Giant forest cockroach *Rhyparobia* sp. (family Blaberidae, spends the day wedged between the bases of dead palm fronds)

Speckled leaf cockroach *Gyna* sp. (family Blaberidae, rests on leaves with head, antennae & legs tucked in)

Masked forest cockroach *Gyna* sp. (family Blaberidae)

White borderd forest cockroach *Gyna* sp. (family Blaberidae)

True bugs belong to the order Hemiptera, which consists of two suborders: Heteroptera (wings folded flat over the abdomen) and Homoptera (wings held tent-like over the abdomen). Some scientists argue that these should be classified as two separate orders. Bed bugs (Cimicidae) belong to Heteroptera but are wingless. Bugs are extremely diverse in both terrestrial and aquatic habitats. They are either predators (usually of other arthropods) or feed on plant sap. The mouthparts of bugs are specialized for piercing and sucking and can be very long. This proboscis or rostrum is usually held flat between the legs, along the underside of the body when not feeding.

Hemiptera is the largest insect order that does not have larval and pupal stages (as in beetles, flies, butterflies, etc.). The young, called nymphs, are basically small, wingless replicas of the adults. Many species are highly cryptic (well camouflaged) whereas others are brightly coloured to warn potential predators that they taste bad (aposematic warning coloration) or that they have a painful bite. Apparently, the bite symptoms of some assassin bugs can remain troublesome for several months. The cicada, which holds the title of being the noisiest insect in the world, will certainly be heard on every trip into the forest. However, they are extremely well camouflaged and difficult spot. It is almost impossible to locate an individual by trying to follow the sound.

Several species are of economic importance as pests of edible crops, ornamentals and cotton (e.g., scale insects, whiteflies, aphids, shield bugs, cotton stainers, etc.), but only a handful of species are of potential medical importance in The Gambia (e.g., bed bugs and assassin bugs). The latter bite readily and should not be handled!

Axe-head cicada *Oxypleura* sp.
(family Cicadidae, wingspan 90 mm)

Green cicada *Afzeliada* sp. (family Cicadidae, the noisiest insects in the world)

Cicada exuvium (shed skin) on leaf
(nymphs feed on roots, have large forelegs
for digging & can take 10 years to mature)

Whitefly (family Aleyrodidae, 3 mm long,
live in large groups & are a pest of various
crops, pictured here on *Carica papaya*)

Soft brown scale insect *Coccus hesperidum*
(family Coccidae, being tended for their
sugary secretions by *Crematogaster* ants)

Long-winged snout bug *Proutista fritillaris*
(family Derbidae, often found in large
numbers on the underside of leaves)

Palm snout bug *Diostrombus* sp. (family
Derbidae, beneath palm fronds)

Long-snouted plant hopper ?*Putala* sp.
(family Dictyopharidae)

Moth bug *Cryptoflata* sp. (family Flatidae, jump well but are weak fliers, found in various habitats from forests to gardens)

Leafhopper (family Cicadellidae, excellent jumpers, highly host-specific herbivores, many species transmit plant diseases)

Spittle bug (family Cercopidae, nymph lives in a ball of spittle made from air mixed with sap-derived anal secretions)

Rain-tree bug *Ptyelus* sp. (family Cercopidae, processed tree sap drips constantly through the bodies of clusters of nymphs & adults)

Twig wilter *Anoplocnemis curvipes* (family Coreidae, saliva causes shoots to shrivel)

Leaf-footed bug *Leptoglossus membranaceus* (family Coreidae, common on loofahs)

Stick water scorpion *Ranatra* sp. (family Nepidae, abdomen has 5 cm breathing siphon, usually found on aquatic vegetation)

Sunflower seed bug *Agonoscelis versicoloratus* (family Pentatomidae, feeds on seeds of developing sunflowers, 12 mm)

Green vegetable bug *Nezara viridula* (family Pentatomidae, a common pest in gardens & agricultural land, 12 mm)

Bagrada bug *Bagrada hilaris* (family Pentatomidae, a problematic pest species of various crops, including groundnuts, 6 mm)

Yellow stink bug *Priassus* sp. ?*exemptus* (family Pentatomidae, 14 mm)

Three spot shield bug *Aspavia armigera* (family Pentatomidae, 6 mm)

Broad-headed bug *Mirperus* sp.
(family Alydidae, alert & active,
on leaf surfaces in forest shade, 14 mm)

Slender broad-headed bug *Stenocoris
apicalis* (Alydidae, has strong smelling
defensive secretion, tropical forests, 14 mm)

Flower assassin bug *Rhinocoris* sp. (family
Reduviidae, ambushes honey bees & insects
at flowers, bite very painful, 18 mm)

Metallic assassin bug *Glymmatophora* sp.
(family Reduviidae, a nocturnal predator,
possibly of millipedes, 15 mm)

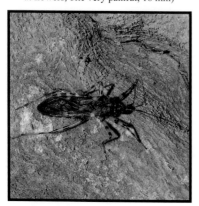

Assassin bug *Reduvius* sp. (family
Reduviidae, a predator with a painful bite!)

Reduvius sp. nymph on tree trunk,
camouflaged with detritus & insect carcases

Milkweed bug *Spilostethus pandurus*
(family Lygaeidae, common in various
habitats, minor pest of sunflowers, 13 mm)

Plant bug *Stalagmostethus furcatus*
(family Lygaeidae, clearly visible so
probably distasteful to predators, 14 mm)

Cotton stainer *Dysdercus fasciatus*
(Largidae, transmits fungus to cotton which
stains the lint yellow or brown, 17 mm)

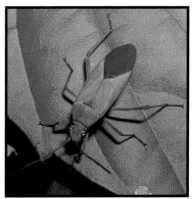

Red-eyed bug *Dysdercus* sp. (Largidae,
very common at certain times of the year,
abdomen bright red, obvious in flight)

Flat bug (family Lophopidae, easily
recognized by their flattened appearance)

Rainbow bug *Callidea duodecimpunctata*
(family Scutelleridae, a magnificent insect!)

Grasshoppers and crickets (order Orthoptera) form a large and diverse order of medium to large insects. Most have well developed hind legs, specialized for jumping and many species have special stridulatory structures to attract mates by sound. Some will be heard chirping away throughout the day, whereas others are nocturnal. Apparently, the call of *Brachytrupes membranaceus* can be heard from a distance of 1.5 km! Some species are distasteful to predators and have warning colouration, others are cryptic. The famous desert locust *Schistocerca gregaria* (Acrididae) belongs to this order and is occasionally responsible for millions of dollars worth of agricultural destruction in Africa, resulting in a great deal of human suffering. A single swarm may contain many millions of individuals. The last invasion in The Gambia was in 2004/5 and affected 230 villages.

Brown grasshopper *Pyrgomorpha vignaudi* (family Pyrgomorphidae, a small cryptic species, tips of vegetation or flower heads)

Variegated locust *Zonocerus variegatus* (family Pyrgomorphidae, body length up to 50 mm, gregarious, in vegetation)

Common stick grasshopper *Acrida acuminata* (family Acrididae, in long grass)

Locusts *Acanthacris ruficornis* mating (Acrididae, strong legs with sharp spines!)

Burrowing grasshopper *Acrotylus* sp.
(Acrididae, bulging eyes, long middle legs
used to dig, in open disturbed areas)

Homeogryllus reticulatus (Phalangopsidae,
female, note the long, thin ovipositor used
for laying eggs, nocturnal)

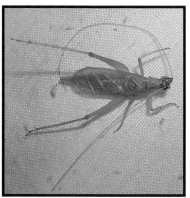

Tree cricket *Oecanthus* sp. (family
Gryllidae, chirp rate depends on ambient
temperature, leaves used to amplify sound)

Brachytrupes membranaceus (family
Gryllidae, beneath logs & stones, 70 mm,
the largest & loudest cricket in the world)

Scaly cricket (family Mogoplistidae,
nocturnal & wingless, with long cerci)

Leaf katydid *Phaneroptera* sp. (family
Tettigoniidae, a minor pest of vegetables)

Lacewings (order Neuroptera) are very common as evidenced from the larval antlion (family Myrmeleontidae) pits visible in most sandy areas. These consist of funnels within the sand, at the bottom of which resides a voracious larva. The pits are constructed so that the slope is at a critical angle. When stepped on by a wandering ant (or other insect), the side gives way, causing the ant to tumble downwards into the large jaws of the hungry larva waiting below. Other neuropterans include owl flies (family Ascalaphidae), which adopt very unusual resting positions on twigs or plant stems, mantis flies (family Mantispidae), which look like small mantids with delicate, lacey wings, and green, brown, dusty, etc. lacewings (various families). Most Neuroptera are very weak flyers, adults are usually predators. Larvae have a sealed anus and do not excrete until in adult form.

Grassland antlion *Cueta* sp. (family Myrmeleontidae, one of the smaller species, a relatively weak flyer, wingspan 58 mm)

Giant antlion *Palpares tigris* (family Myrmeleontidae, open grassland, wingspan more than 100 mm, larvae roam in sand)

Bark antlion adult *Centroclisis* sp. (family Myrmeleontidae, a large species with a wingspan of approximately 85 mm, larvae probably live in sand at the base of trees)

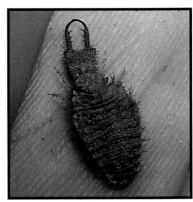

Pit-building antlion *Myrmeleon* sp. (family Myrmeleontidae, small, one of the more primitive antlions, wingspan 45 mm)

Larva of antlion *Myrmeleon* sp. (family Myrmeleontidae, you can often see them excavating their pits, note the large jaws)

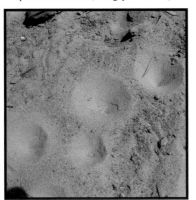

Pits of antlion *Myrmeleon* sp. (family Myrmeleontidae, very common, unfortunate prey tumble down to the hungry larva)

Broad-winged green lacewing *Dichochrysa sjoestedti* (Chrysopidae, on forest vegetation, wingspan 30 mm)

Owl fly (family Ascalaphidae) in typical resting position, flies at dusk

Mantis fly (family Mantispidae, an example of convergent evolution with mantids)

Termites (order Isoptera) live in large colonies and are highly social animals. Particularly large termite mounds may exceed 4 m in height and exist for decades, possibly centuries in some species. Beware, these mounds often serve as a refuge for snakes, bats and other animals to escape the heat of the day, so never poke your hand in one! Smaller termitaria can also be seen in the forks of tree branches. Some ants (*Crematogaster* spp.) make similar structures, but only termites construct the tell-tale covered trails leading from the nest. Termites can be found under any piece of rotting wood, where they recycle the cellulose cell walls, achieved by symbiotic micro-organisms that live in their guts. They are serious pests of wooden structures and various crops (accounting for losses of 15–90%). Number of species in Gambia unknown, 64 recorded from Senegal.

Worker fungus-growing termites *Odontotermes* sp. (family Termitidae, the most destructive termite of wooden homes)

Winged adult termite *Odontotermes* sp. (family Termitidae, large swarms emerge shortly after first rains, attracted to lights)

Termite mound (note the man standing on top for scale!)

Arboreal termite construction with covered trails leading from the nest

Other insects that you might encounter include **preying mantises** (order Mantodea), which are easily identified by their heavily spined raptorial forelegs that they hold in a prayer-like manner and use for catching prey. All are active by day (diurnal) and are ambush predators, relying on stealth to sneak up on their victims. When suitably close, they snap out their front legs to catch the unsuspecting insect which is then held firmly in a vice-like grip allowing the strong mandibles to get to work on consuming the meal.

Many species have elaborate projections on their heads and some have flap-like cuticular outgrowths on the legs. One species resembles a stick insect, but the raptorial front legs, large eyes and alert behaviour belie its true identity. When threatened, the eyed mantis will flash open its hindwings in an attempt to deter the aggressor. In some species the female eats the male during copulation. Nymphs often differ in appearance from the adults. How many species occur in The Gambia is unclear, but they appear to be rather diverse. Adults have been known to give a painful (but not venomous) bite when handled inappropriately.

Earwigs (order Dermaptera) are relatively common and are easily identified by the presence of a pair of posterior curved forceps on the abdomen. These are used for prey capture, display or for unfolding the elaborately folded hindwings, which usually remain concealed beneath the tiny, hardened forewings when not in use. The forceps are often more developed in males and are usually, but not always symmetrical. Most species prefer damp places and are nocturnal, but they are sometimes found wandering around during the day, particularly when overcast. Most are scavengers and eat various foodstuffs, but some catch other insects with their forceps. There are no known reports of earwigs ever having ventured into the ear of a human and they are totally harmless.

Web spinners (order Embioptera) have both winged (males of some species) and wingless (female) adults and are easily identified by having thickened leg segments at the tip of the first pair of legs. These are packed full of special glands, which they use to make silk. Most web spinners live in small colonies in silk-lined galleries beneath bark, logs, stones or in curled up leaves. They eat lichens, bark, mosses and dead plant material and exhibit a degree of maternal behaviour, but little else is known of their biology. Males are attracted to lights and so often enter houses. Females of one species are also sometimes found in houses, others occur in forests.

Common green mantis *Sphodromantis* sp. (Mantodea, family Mantidae, nymphs lack wings & curl abdomen over body, 55 mm)

Stick mantis *Danuria* sp. (order Mantodea, family Mantidae, easy to mistake for a stick insect at first sight, 50 mm)

Small pale green mantis *Miomantis* sp. (order Mantodea, family Mantidae, nymphs of some species mimic ants, 25 mm)

Bark mantis ?*Tarachodes* sp. (order Mantodea, family Mantidae, on twigs & trunks but cryptic & difficult to see, 35 mm)

Mantid egg case, eggs laid in a frothy mass which dries to form the hardened ootheca

Flat mantis *Elaea marchali* (Family Mantidae, on bark & underside of logs)

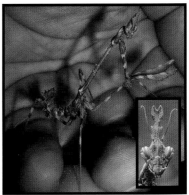

Eyed-flower mantis *Pseudocreobotra occellata* (family Hymenopodidae, on flowers, flash their wings to deter predators)

Gargoyle mantis *Empusa* sp. (family Empusidae, wingless juvenile, a large mantis on various types of vegetation)

Long-horned earwig *Euborellia annulipes* (order Dermaptera, family Labiduridae, wingless, damp habitats, body 20 mm)

Long-horned earwig *Labidura riparia* (order Dermaptera, Labiduridae, in defensive posture, under wood & stones, body 30 mm)

Common earwig *Forficula senegalensis* (Dermaptera, family Forficulidae, 8 mm)

Web spinner *Apterembia* sp. (order Embioptera, family Embiidae, body 14 mm)

Beetles (order Coleoptera) are the most diverse animal group on the planet in terms of numbers of described species (370,000+) and there is much variation in colour, form, size and behaviour. Coleoptera includes both the smallest and largest known living insects. All beetles have highly sclerotized (hardened) forewings which are called elytra. These form a protective casing over the abdomen (although in some families they are much reduced) and protect the delicate, membranous hindwings, which are neatly folded beneath them and used for flight. In some families the elytra are fused together along the midline, so these beetles are unable to fly (for example, in the seedpod beetle illustrated, which looks nothing like an insect when viewed from above). However, most beetles are relatively good fliers and are found in most habitats, including aquatic ones.

Many beetles are dull black or brown (many Tenebrionidae), but others are quite striking with metallic blues, reds and greens (e.g., some Chrysomelidae and Cerambycidae). In some species males and females are difficult to distinguish from one another, whereas in others sexual dimorphism is very pronounced (e.g., Ripiphoridae). The mouthparts of beetles are adapted for chewing. True bugs (Hemiptera), which many people often confuse for beetles have a long, piercing rostrum designed for sucking up fluids. Beetle larvae are variable, but again, all have biting mouthparts and a well sclerotized head.

The Gambia is home to many beetle species, although the fauna is poorly known. Blister beetles (family Meloidae) are particularly common and diverse. Their bodies contain a chemical that can cause blistering of the skin so they should not be handled (many of them have bright warning colours indicating they should be left alone). Some species, such as tiger beetles have excellent vision and are voracious predators, whereas others feed on plant matter, detritus, dung, animal carcasses or are parasites of other animals. Other beetles likely to be seen include the flower and fruit chafers (Scarabaeidae). These are medium-sized, often brightly coloured and usually seen feeding on flower heads. Look carefully on the butterfly bush *Lantana camara* (page 28) and you should see several species.

Many of the beetles illustrated here are new records for the country and you will certainly see additional species not in this field guide. I would be very grateful to receive nice photos of them (email address inside the front cover).

Maroon & yellow flower chafer
Macroma cognata
(family Scarabaeidae)

Large black-nest chafer
Diplognatha gagates
(family Scarabaeidae)

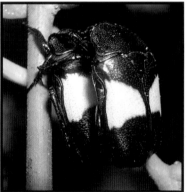

Yellow-belted flower chafers mating
Chondrorrhina abbreviata
(family Scarabaeidae)

Flame-sided flower chafer
Gametis sanguinolenta
(family Scarabaeidae)

Grass chafer *Gnathocera varians*
(family Scarabaeidae)

Flower chafer *Phonotaenia* sp.
(family Scarabaeidae)

Tri-coloured flower chafer
Pachnoda cordata
(family Scarabaeidae)

Black & red flower chafer
Pachnoda interrupta
(family Scarabaeidae)

Smooth chafer
Anomala sp.
(family Scarabaeidae)

Large rhinoceros beetle
Oryctes boas
(family Scarabaeidae, feeds on palm juice)

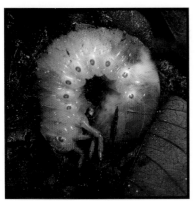

Unidentified beetle larva
(probably from the family Scarabaeidae)

Dung beetle (family Scarabaeidae, may be
seen pushing dung along forest trails)

Click beetle *Alaus excavatus* (Elateridae, leap into the air as an escape mechanism, making a loud click in the process)

Newly hatched jewel beetle *Sphenoptera* sp. (family Buprestidae, more mature specimens are black & shiny)

Wedge-headed beetle *Macrosiagon ?axillare* (family Ripiphoridae, note the tiny male beneath the female)

Wedge-headed beetle *Macrosiagon ?axillare* (family Ripiphoridae, close up of the tiny male in the previous photograph)

Water scavenger beetle *Hydrophilus picicornis* (family Hydrophilidae)

Lunate ladybird *?Ceilomenes* sp. (family Coccinellidae, feeds on aphids)

Burrowing ground beetle *Scarites senegalensis* (family Carabidae, adults burrow in soil where they hunt insect larvae)

Giant ground beetle *Tefflus megerlei* (family Carabidae, large predator with a body length of almost 5 cm)

Maroon tiger beetles *Ropaloteres cinctus* mating (family Cicindelidae, early rainy season, readily take to the wing)

Leopard tiger beetle *Lophyra senegalensis* (family Cicindelidae, open sandy areas, very small and very fast)

Metallic longhorn beetle *Rhopalizus* sp. (family Cerambycidae: Callichromatini)

Bird dropping longhorn *Apopmecyna ?alboannulata* (Cerambycidae: Lamiinae)

Slender net-winged beetle *Lycus sinuatus* (family Lycidae, contain the chemical cantharadin so distasteful to predators)

Tailed net-winged beetle *Lycus trabeatus* (family Lycidae, feeds on flowers including those of trees, often found in large numbers)

Seedpod beetle *Endustomus senegalensis* (family Tenebrionidae, usually found motionless in leaf litter or under logs)

Mouldy beetle *Pogonobasis* sp. (Tenebrionidae, sand particles used as camouflage, held in place by waxy hairs)

Darkling beetle *Pimelia senegalensis* (family Tenebrionidae)

Red-rimmed beetle *Praeugena* sp. (family Tenebrionidae)

Spiky ground beetle
Vieta senegalensis
(family Tenebrionidae)

Metallic groove-winged flower beetle
Melyris sp. (family Melyridae, feed on
pollen but also visit carcasses & dung)

Black spotted tortoise beetle
Aspidimorpha nigropunctata
(family Chrysomelidae: Cassidinae)

Fool's gold tortoise beetle
Aspidimorpha quinquefasciata
(family Chrysomelidae, common)

Red tortoise beetle *Aspidimorpha areata*
(family Chrysomelidae, common)

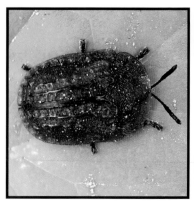

Wrinkled tortoise beetle *Laccoptera
corrugata* (family Chrysomelidae)

Black and red leaf beetle *Clytra notata*
(family Chrysomelidae, some specimens
also have a black spot on the thorax)

Mating leaf beetles
Mesoplatys cincta
(family Chrysomelidae: Chrysomelinae)

Green leaf beetle
Colaposoma sp.
(family Chrysomelidae: Eumolpinae)

Orange-headed blister beetle *Epicauta
nigromaculata* (family Meloidae, usually
seen on grasses)

Three-banded blister beetle *Coryna
apicornis* (family Meloidae)

Two-banded blister beetle *Mylabris
bifasciata* (family Meloidae)**

Spotted blister beetle
Mylabris sp.
(family Meloidae)

Wave-banded blister beetle
Mylabris sp.
(family Meloidae)

Felt blister beetle
Mylabris pallipes
(family Meloidae)

Mating weevils
?*Hadromerus sagittarius*
(family Curculionidae)

Weevil *Alcidodes haemopterus*
(family Curculionidae)

Red-legged weevil *Temnoschoita* sp.
(family Curculionidae)

Armoured weevil *Brachycerus* sp.
(family Curculionidae, feeding on fireball
lily fruit *Scadoxus multifloris*)

Thick-legged weevil
Hadromerus sp.
(family Curculionidae)

Big-eyed weevil *Osphilia* sp.
(family Curculionidae, feeding at wound on
baobab tree)

Yellow weevil *Lixus* sp.
(Curculionidae, a relatively large weevil,
lies on back & feigns death when disturbed)

Grass weevils *Aorus* sp.
(family Curculionidae)

Diamond-spot weevil *Gasteroclisus*
rhomboidalis (family Curculionidae)

Both **moths and butterflies** (order Lepidoptera) are diverse in The Gambia. The latter are day-active and more apparent and for this reason they have been studied in some detail. Approximately 170 species have been recorded, but it is still possible to find new species records for the country. However, these will almost certainly have been recorded previously from nearby countries, such as Senegal. There are some day-flying (diurnal) moths, many of which are brightly coloured. The majority though are small, nocturnal and highly cryptic during the day. To provide an estimate of moth species richness for The Gambia is not easy, although I was reliably informed by a lepidopterist that a ratio of ten moth species for every butterfly species is not an unreasonable expectation.

There is no clear, unequivocal morphological distinction between butterflies and moths, although the former usually have distinctly clubbed antennae, whereas various forms occur in moths. Both are characterized by having two pairs of large wings, which along with the body, are covered in fine scales. It is these scales that produce the elaborate colours, with metallic and iridescent hues resulting from fine grooves and ridges which diffract the light. The mouthparts are usually elongated to form a long, sucking proboscis, which remains coiled up when not in use. In many species this proboscis can be several times longer than the body when fully extended.

Lepidoptera undergo a life cycle of egg to caterpillar to pupa and finally adult. The larvae are usually herbivores. Many caterpillars have long hairs that can irritate human skin and are a defense against predators. In moths the pupa is usually covered with a silky cocoon, absent in butterflies. Some species are present year round, others appear for a limited spell, usually during the rainy season.

In some species, such as the citrus swallowtail the two sexes are similar in appearance, but in others there is great sexual dimorphism and the two sexes could easily be mistaken for different species. Some butterflies employ self-mimicry, whereby they have one body part that resembles another. The hindwings contain eyespots and tails that wave around in the breeze, resembling antennae. Many predators would attack this region first in order to achieve a quick kill, thinking it was the head. In many cases, this gives the butterfly the split second it needs to escape before the predator realizes the deception. Indeed, look carefully and you will see many such butterflies flying around missing sections of their hind wings.

Crimson-speckled footman *Utethesia pulchella* (family Arctiidae, diurnal, common, especially on *Crotalaria* flowers)

Tiger moth *Ardices* (*Spilosoma*) *maculosus* (family Arctiidae, warning colouration indicates it is distasteful to predators)

Maiden moth *Syntomis* sp. (family Arctiidae: Ctenuchinae, diurnal, usually seen resting on the underside of leaves)

Hornet moths *Euchromia ?formosa* mating (family Arctiidae: Ctenuchinae, diurnal, common, slow flyer, wingspan 40 mm)[++]

White pearl *Palpita* sp. (family Crambidae: Spilomelinae, wingspan 30 mm)

Brown owlet moth *Cyligramma fluctuosa* (family Noctuidae, wingspan 75 mm)

Oleander hawk moth *Daphnis nerii* (family Sphingidae, wingspan 110 mm, larvae feed on oleander, jasmine & mango)[++]

Common striped hawk moth *Hippotion esson* (family Sphingidae, wingspan 75 mm, common in various habitats)

Common nephele *Nephele comma* (family Sphingidae, wingspan 75 mm, forewing often with white comma mark)

Silver-striped hawk moth *Hippotion celerio* (family Sphingidae, wingspan 75 mm, common in various habitats)

Arrow sphinx *Lophostethus dumolinii*[++] (family Sphingidae, wingspan 140 mm)

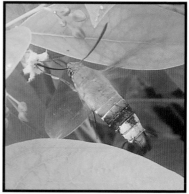

Oriental bee hawk *Cephonodes hylas* (family Sphingidae, wingspan 70 mm)

Convolvulus hawk moth *Agrius convolvuli* (family Sphingidae, wingspan 100 mm, common migrant sometimes also in Europe)

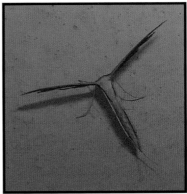

Plume moth (family Pterophoridae, small moths easily identified by the way they hold their wings at rest: T or Y shaped)

Southern atlas silkmoth *Epiphora bauhiniae* (family Saturnidae, large impressive moth with a wingspan of more than 100 mm)

Flower moth (family Scythrididae, tiny moth, antennae with thick base, hindwings bright red & flashed to deter predators)

Larva & pupa of bagworm moth *Clania* sp. (Psychidae, adult moths seldom seen)

Silky lappet moth (family Lasiocampidae, very hairy & with silky appearance)

Forester or false tiger moth ?*Heraclia* sp. (family Noctuidae: Agaristinae, wingspan 60 mm, a diurnal moth of forest habitats)

Grass moth *Crameria amabilis* (family Noctuidae: Agaristinae, wingspan 30 mm, common in short coastal scrub vegetation)

Brown-bordered moth *Zamarada* sp. (family Geometridae, wingspan 25 mm, common in urban areas)

Highly cryptic nocturnal moth ?*Idaea* sp. (family Geometridae: Ennominae, wingspan 15 mm)

Duster moth *Pingasa* sp. (family Geometridae, wingspan 40 mm, common in ubran areas)

Common hairstreak *Hypolycaena philippus*
(family Lycaenidae: Theclinae,
wingspan 33 mm)

Common hairstreak *Hypolycaena philippus*
(family Lycaenidae: Theclinae, very
common, larvae polyphagous)

Common scarlet *Axiocerses harpax*
(family Lycaenidae: Theclinae,
wingspan 35 mm, rapid flyer)

Common scarlet *Axiocerses harpax*
(family Lycaenidae: Theclinae, hindwing
markings reduced in dry season form)

Common brown playboy *Deudorix antalus*
(family Lycaenidae: Theclinae, ws 36 mm)

Common brown playboy *Deudorix antalus*
(family Lycaenidae: Theclinae)

Common fig blue *Myrina silenus silenus* (family Lycaenidae: Theclinae, wingspan 38 mm, upperside royal blue, black margin)

Pea blue *Lampides boeticus* (family Lycaenidae: Polyommatinae, wingspan 35 mm, underside pattern highly distinctive)

Common grass blue *Zizeeria knysna* (family Lycaenidae: Polyommatinae, wingspan 24 mm, male, female dark brown)

Common grass blue *Zizeeria knysna* (family Lycaenidae: Polyommatinae, very common, usually flying at ground level)

Dark grass blue *Zizina antanossa* (Lycaenidae: Polyommatinae, ws 26 mm)

Common bush blue *Cacyreus lingeus* (Lycaenidae: Polyommatinae, ws 30 mm)

Common ciliate blue *Anthene larydas*
(family Lycaenidae: Polyommatinae,
wingspan 29 mm, male, female back/brown)

Common ciliate blue underside
(family Lycaenidae: Polyommatinae, larvae
feed on *Albizia*, *Acacia* & *Dicrostachys*)

Mediterranean pierrot *Tarucus rosacea*
(Lycaenidae: Polyommatinae, wingspan
24 mm, larvae on *Zizyphus*)

Savannah pied pierrot *Tuxentius cretosus
nodieri* (family Lycaenidae: Polyommatinae,
wingspan 31 mm, larvae on *Zizyphus*)

Common zebra blue *Leptotes ?pirithous*[++]
(Lycaenidae: Polyommatinae, male)

Common zebra blue *Leptotes ?pirithous*
(Lycaenidae: Polyommatinae, ws 31 mm)

Smoky bean cupid *Euchrysops malathana*
(family Lycaenidae: Polyommatinae,
wingspan 31 mm, larvae pupate in ant nest)

African cupid *Euchrysops osiris*
(family Lycaenidae: Polyommatinae,
wingspan 31 mm, both sexes with tails)

Grass jewel *Chilades trochylus*
(family Lycaenidae: Polyommatinae,
wingspan 20 mm, upperside a warm brown)

Untailed blue giant cupid *Lepidochrysops
synchrematiza* (family Lycaenidae, in open
habitats, wingspan 45 mm)

Desert babul blue *Azanus ubaldus*
(Lycaenidae: Polyommatinae, ws 24 mm)

Leaden ciliate blue *Anthene amarah*
(Lycaenidae: Polyommatinae, ws 26 mm)

Twin swift *Borbo gemella*
(family Hesperiidae: Hesperiinae, wingspan
36 mm, short grass savanna, widespread)

Olive-haired swift *Borbo b. borbonica*
(family Hesperiidae: Hesperiinae, wingspan
42 mm, big skipper with pointed forewings)

Common hopper *Platylesches moritili*
(family Hesperiidae: Hesperiinae, wingspan
33 mm, often seen resting on *Neocarya*)

Lesser millet skipper *Pelopidas mathias*
(family Hesperiidae: Hesperiinae, wingspan
38 mm, most common Gambian skipper)

Common crepuscular skipper *Gretna waga*
(Hesperiidae: Hesperiinae, ws 48 mm)

Striped policeman *Coeliades forestan*
(Hesperiidae: Coeliadinae, ws 54 mm)

Diomus grizzled skipper *Spialia diomus*
(family Hesperiidae: Pyrginae, wingspan
29 mm, one of three very similar species)

Grey elfin *Sarangesa laelius*
(family Hesperiidae: Pyrginae, wingspan
36 mm, rests on ground with wings flat)

Orange acraea *Acraea serena*** (family
Nymphalidae: Heliconiinae, male, wingspan
42 mm, female similar but drab brown)

Large spotted acraea *Acraea zetes zetes*
(family Nymphalidae: Heliconiinae,
wingspan 74 mm, male, female duller)

Common leopard *Phalantha p. aethiopica*
(Nymphalidae: Heliconiinae, ws 57 mm)

Variable eggfly *Hypolimnas a. anthedon*
(Nymphalidae: Nymphalinae, ws 84 mm)

Male diadem *Hypolimnas misippus*
(family Nymphalidae: Nymphalinae,
wingspan 76 mm, common, many habitats)

Female diadem *Hypolimnas misippus*
(family Nymphalidae: Nymphalinae,
wingspan 76 mm, mimic of *D. chrysippus*)

Dark blue pansy *Junonia oenone oenone*
(family Nymphalidae: Nymphalinae,
wingspan 56 mm, very common)

Little commodore *Junonia sophia sophia*
(family Nymphalidae: Nymphalinae,
wingspan 49 mm, disturbed habitats)

African painted lady *Vanessa cardui cardui*
(Nymphalidae: Nymphalinae, ws 65 mm)

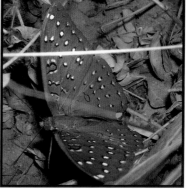

Guineafowl *Hamanumida daedalus*
(Nymphalidae: Limenitidinae, ws 66 mm)

African tiger *Danaus c. chrysippus*
(family Nymphalidae: Danainae, wingspan
84 mm, common year round in all habitats)

Pearl charax *Charaxes varanes vologeses*
(family Nymphalidae: Charaxinae,
wingspan 90 mm, upperside orange/white)

Male African emigrant *Catopsilia florella*
(family Pieridae: Coliadinae, wingspan
70 mm, migrants often larger, common)

Female African emigrant *Catopsilia florella*
(sometimes similar colour to male, yellow
morphs seen more often during migrations)

Small grass yellow *Eurema brigitta brigitta*
(family Pieridae: Coliadinae)***

Small grass yellow *Eurema brigitta brigitta*
(Pieridae: Coliadinae, wingspan 38 mm)

Common grass yellow *Eurema hecabe* (Pieridae: Coliadinae, black tip of forewing obvious in flight, wingspan 41 mm)

Common dotted border *Mylothris c. chloris* (family Pieridae: Pierinae, wingspan 64 mm, male with thinner black band on hindwing)

African caper white *Belenois creona creona* (family Pieridae: Pierinae, wingspan 58 mm, a common migratory species)

African caper white *Belenois creona creona* (family Pieridae: Pierinae, larval foodplants include *Capparis*, *Ritchiea* & others)

Calypso caper white *Belenois c. calypso* (Pieridae: Pierinae, wingspan 66 mm)

Caper white *Belenois aurota* (Pieridae: Pierinae, wingspan 57 mm)

Male creamy small white *Dixiea orbona* (family Pieridae: Pierinae, wingspan 46 mm, female underside often yellow)

Female creamy small white *Dixiea orbona* (Pieridae: Pierinae, often seen landing on leaves & raising abdomen to attract males)

Zebra white *Pinacopteryx eriphia tritogenia* (family Pieridae: Pierinae, sexes similar, sometimes seen in large migratory swarms)

Zebra white *Pinacopteryx eriphia tritogenia*++ (family Pieridae: Pierinae, wingspan 48 mm, smaller in dry season)

African spirit *Leptosia alcesta alcesta* (Pieridae: Pierinae, wingspan 40 mm)

Scarlet tip *Colotis danae eupompe* (Pieridae: Pierinae, wingspan 46 mm)

Large orange tip *Colotis a. antevippe*
(family Pieridae: Pierinae, wingspan
52 mm, common, often in large numbers)

Tiny orange tip *Colotis evagore antigone***
(family Pieridae: Pierinae, wingspan
34 mm, both sexes highly variable)

Narrow-banded green swallowtail *Papilio nireus nireus*[++] (family Papilionidae, wingspan 115 mm, usually seen in forests)

Citrus swallowtail *Papilio d. demodocus*
(family Papilionidae, wingspan 105 mm,
very common in all habitats, sexes similar)

Veined swallowtail *Graphium l. leonidas*
(family Papilionidae, wingspan 95 mm)

White lady *Graphium angolanus baronis*
(family Papilionidae, wingspan 85 mm)

Ants (order Hymenoptera: Formicidae) are ubiquitous in tropical forests and it has been suggested by some scientists that they may account for almost 10 percent of the total forest biomass. At least 60 ant species have been recorded from The Gambia, but given that 2,500 or so species have been described from the African continent, their true diversity can be expected to be greater than this.

A single ant species consists of several different castes (e.g., queen, drones, workers and sometimes soldiers), each of which has a different morphology, suited to perform a different function for the benefit of the colony. Drones mate with the queen, which produces the eggs, while soldiers protect the colony and workers as they go about their duties gathering food and tending to the young. Ants are highly social insects with well-developed methods of communication, utilizing both tactile and chemical stimuli. Many species feed on sugary secretions produced by true bugs. They do not harm the insects and often 'farm' them in large numbers.

A particularly common species is the weaver ant. This species forms nests by binding leaves together with larval silk. They are highly alert, ready to defend themselves against any intruder, using their large mandibles and formic acid, which is sprayed from the abdomen. They are often seen harassing any unfortunate insect that has strayed close to their nest.

The larger black ants, which are commonly seen wandering as solitary individuals on forest trails live in small colonies. They do not spray formic acid, but pack a powerful sting! Note that some spiders are excellent ant mimics, even to the point of holding their first pair of legs aloft and waving them around like insect antennae.

Queen weaver ant *Oecophylla longinoda* (Formicinae, starting a new colony)

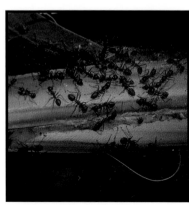

Worker weaver ants bind leaves together using silk produced by the larvae

African stink ant *Pachycondyla (Paltothyreus) tarsata* (subfamily Ponerinae, lives in small colonies, often seen alone)

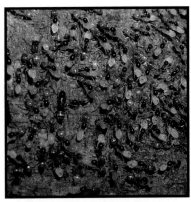

Tapinoma melanocephalum on the move: workers carrying eggs, larvae and pupae (subfamily Dolichoderinae)

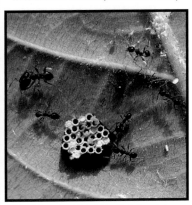

Pheidole aeberlii (subfamily Myrmicinae, harvesting insect eggs under the protection of a large-headed soldier

Lepisiota gerardi (subfamily Formicinae, milking the sugary secretions from a palm scale insect (Hemiptera)

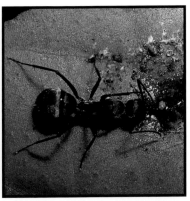

Saddled ant *Camponotus (Myrmosericus) flavomarginatus* (subfamily Formicinae)

Workers, soldier & drones of *Camponotus (Tanaemyrmex) maculatus* (Formicinae)

Closely allied to the ants (belonging to the same order, Hymenoptera) are the **sawflies, bees and wasps**. Many of these also live in colonies, but some species are solitary. Some are specialist parasites of spiders or other insects. One interesting example of this is the emerald cockroach wasp *Ampulex compressa* which uses cockroaches as hosts for its developing offspring. These are large wasps, but still they are not strong enough to carry the large cockroaches they provide as food for their developing young and have evolved a remarkable way of overcoming this problem. Firstly the wasp stings the cockroach in a specific nerve ganglion in the thorax, which semi-paralyzes the front pair of legs. This is followed by a second sting, into the brain, which inhibits the escape reflex of the cockroach. The wasp leads the prey by its antenna, the cockroach walking under its own effort.

Rose sawfly *Arge* sp. (family Argidae, different suborder from other Hymenoptera, characterized by lacking a constricted waist)

Stingless or sweat bees *?Hypotrigona* sp. (family Apidae) in waxy nest entrance on a tree trunk, collect moisture from humans

Honey bee *Apis melifera adansoni* (family Apidae, kept for honey production)

Bee honeycomb (*Apis melifera adansoni*) hanging from a tree

Female carpenter bee *Xylocopa callens* (family Apidae; formerly Anthophoridae, excavates nest burrows in wood and trees)

Male carpenter bee *Xylocopa callens* (family Apidae; formerly Anthophoridae, large bee with body length of 25 mm)

?*Megachile* sp. (family Megachilidae, sleeps with mandibles embedded in grass stems)

Cuckoo wasp *Chrysis* sp. (family Chrysididae, lay eggs in nests of other solitary bees or wasps, adults feed on nectar)

Semi-social flower bee *Nomia* sp. (family Halictidae, nests below ground)

Beetle wasp (family Tiphiidae) (parasites of subterranean beetle larvae)

Thread-waisted wasp *Ammophila* sp. (family Sphecidae, females hunt caterpillars, widespread in areas with bare sandy soil)

Bee wolf *Philanthus* sp. (family Sphecidae, ambush honey bees at flowers as provision for multi-celled nests in bare, sandy soil)

Sand-digger wasp *Bembecinus* sp. (family Sphecidae, often seen digging in sandy soil in subtropical forest & savanna)

Cockroach wasp *Ampulex compressa* with subdued prey (family Sphecidae, see account of behaviour on page 90)

Mud dauber wasp *Sceliphron spirifex* (family Sphecidae, hunting for spiders)

Mud dauber wasp nest opened to reveal pupa and larva with paralyzed spider prey

Parasitic wasp pupa *Charops* sp. (family Braconidae, suspended from vegetation following larval development in caterpillar)

Parasitic wasp (family Braconidae, species in this family are smaller & stouter than ichneumon wasps, often bright red-orange)

Parasitic wasps *Glyptomorpha* sp. (Braconidae, female has long ovipositor, absent in the male on the right)

Ensign wasp *Evania* sp. (family Evaniidae, note the tiny laterally compressed abdomen, larvae are parasites of cockroach egg cases)

Parasitic wasp *Enicospilus* sp. (family Ichneumonidae, parasitizes moth larvae)

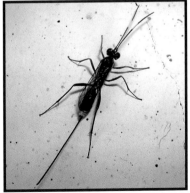

Ichneumon wasp (family Ichneumonidae, long ovipositor used to drill plant stems)

Spider-hunting wasp *Cyphononyx flavicornis* (family Pompilidae, characteristic wing-jerk when hunting)

Large spider hawk wasp *Hemipepsis* sp. (family Pompilidae, with paralyzed prey, usually seen hunting at ground level)

Orange-tipped mason wasp *Anterhynchium synapoide* (family Eumenidae, nests in cavities or empty mud nests of other wasps)

Spherical mud nest of the potter wasp (family Eumenidae, adult similar in appearance to the paper wasp below)

Brown paper wasps *Polistes* sp. (family Vespidae, very common)

Large paper wasps *Belonogaster* sp. (family Vespidae, common, painful sting!)

Flies (order Diptera) are very common in The Gambia. Most insects have four wings, but in true flies the hindwings are reduced to a pair of knob-like structures called halteres. These act in a gyroscopic fashion during flight and move in opposition to the beating wings, thus maintaining balance and facilitating rapid manoeuvrability. Most flies do not impact on humans, others are of great economic or medical importance, some are beneficial. The infamous mosquito spreads malaria and other diseases and is responsible for more than two million deaths each year in Africa. The larvae of many species are parasites of other animals including domestic livestock and humans, with some species living inside the stomach and others under the skin. This condition is termed myiasis and the tumbu or putsi fly is an unpleasant parasite of humans (and other animals) in The Gambia.

Red-headed fly *Peltacanthina albolineata* (family Platystomatidae, signaling with legs, often congregate on exposed leaves)

Moth fly *Clogmia albipunctata* (family Psychodidae, common in urban areas, stop domestic drains from clogging with fungi)

Striped fly *Anthomyia* sp. (family Anthomyiidae, small, wingspan 10 mm)

Numerous tiny (3 mm) gall midges (family Cecidomyiidae, resting on a dead spider)

Fly pirate *Bengalia* sp. (family
Calliphoridae, adults sit by ant trails &
snatch food, eggs & larvae)

Blowflies *Chrysomya* sp. mating
(family Calliphoridae, feed on corpses, but
some species cause myiasis in live animals)

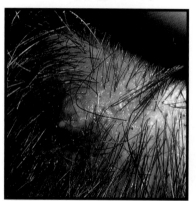

Tumbu fly larva *Cordylobia anthropophaga*
(family Calliphoridae, under author's scalp,
painful at times, wriggled out after 14 days)

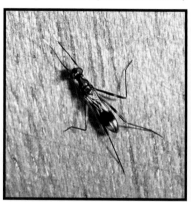

Ichneumon mimic *Mimegralla fuelleborni*
(family Micropezidae, short front legs held
forwards & waved about like antennae)

Robber fly *Promachus* sp. (family Asilidae,
prey on other insects caught during flight)

Robber fly *Microstylum* sp. (family Asilidae,
feeding on another robber fly)

Wasp mimic soldier fly *Hermetia illucens*
(family Stratiomyiidae, urban habitats,
larvae grow in compost heaps)

Hoverfly *Mesembrius* sp. (Syrphidae, a
common bee mimic found in gardens, a very
diverse family of flies)

Hoverflies mating *Ischiodon aegyptius*
(family Syrphidae, common in gardens,
rapid, yet precise hovering flight)

Hoverfly *Asarkina ?ericetorum* (Syrphidae,
a conspicuous wasp mimic, often seen
hovering in sun-lit forest gaps)

Giant forest mosquito
(family Culicidae, wingspan 20 mm)

Hippo fly *Tabanus biguttatus* (family
Tabanidae, attacks large mammals)

Minute jackal flies (family Milichiidae, scavenging leaking juices from spider prey, also near mantids, wasps, robber flies, etc.)

Long-legged flies *Chrysosoma aestimabile* (family Dolichopodidae, tiny & metallic green, gather on upperside of leaves)

Ligyra melanoptera (family Bombyliidae, laying eggs in the sand, the most diverse fly family in Africa)

Small cucurbit fly *Didacus ciliatus* (family Tephritidae, larvae are pests of curcubit fruits such as watermelon, gourds, etc.)

Fruit fly *Ceratitis rosa* (family Tephritidae, a pest of many tropical fruit species)

Fresh monkey dung is a great place to look for flies if you are that way inclined

Additional true insect orders not covered in the current version of this guide, but known (or expected) to be present in The Gambia include: **mayflies** (order Ephemeroptera), **stoneflies** (order Plecoptera), **stick insects** (order Phasmatodea), **booklice** (order Psocoptera), **lice** (order Phthiraptera), **thrips** (order Thysanoptera), **Alderflies** (order Megaloptera), **stylopids** (order Strepsiptera), **hanging flies** (order Mecoptera) and **fleas** (order Siphonaptera).

The majority of these are tiny, relatively scarce or highly cryptic and unlikely to be seen on a regular basis.

SPIDERS

Wherever insects abound so do **spiders** (order Araneae), their major predators. They are not insects, but arachnids (they have only two main body regions and eight legs, not six) and are all obligate predators. They represent the most diverse group of predators in terrestrial ecosystems and are able to produce and utilize silk in more ways than any other animal, but not all of them weave webs.

In excess of 40,000 spider species have been described and this represents only a fraction (possibly about 25%) of the expected total. Of the 108 or so spider families that occur around the world, more than 70 of these can be found in Africa. How many of these occur within The Gambia is unclear as very little research has been done on West African spiders and almost nothing is known about The Gambian fauna. Indeed, many of the photographs here represent the first records of those spider families for the country.

Given the above diversity figures and the fact that only a handful of spiders are of medical importance in terms of being able to inflict a poisonous bite (including some species present in The Gambia), spiders have somewhat of an undeserved bad name. Rather, spiders are extremely beneficial because they kill disease vectors such as mosquitoes and many different types of pest species both within the home and in agricultural settings.

You are most likely to see jumping spiders (Salticidae), which are day active, relatively small, sometimes brightly coloured and have very large front eyes. If visiting during the rainy season or shortly after you cannot fail to miss the giant golden orb-weaving spiders (Nephilidae). Large, flat brown crab spiders (Selenopidae) are often seen on the inside walls of buildings at night and daddy-long-legs spiders (Pholcidae) are common in outside toilets.

Jumping spider *Portia africana* (family Salticidae, a specialist predator of golden orb spiders from the family Nephilidae)

Jumping spider *Meleon solitaria* (family Salticidae, waves legs about in an elaborate courtship display, even to cameras!)

Jumping spider *Holcolaetis vellerea* (family Salticidae, common on tree trunks, but well camouflaged, eats other spiders)

Holcolaetis vellerea consuming a giant crab spider (family Sparassidae) much larger than itself, a potentially lethal prey item

Fat-legged jumping spider *Thyene* sp. (family Salticidae, on vegetation)

Striped jumping spider *Viciria* sp. (family Salticidae, on vegetation)

Red jumping spider *Cyrba* sp.
(family Salticidae, small spider usually
found beneath logs in the forest)

Jumping spider *Menemerus bivittatus*
(family Salticidae, common on trees &
walls, often lurk by stingless bee nests)

Horned jumping spider *Hyllus* sp. (family
Salticidae, this species is particularly
common, found in houses & forests)

Black masked jumping spider *Hyllus* sp.
(family Salticidae, another common species
on vegetation in urban areas)

Smiling coast jumping spider *Telamonia* sp.
(family Salticidae, note smile on abdomen!)

Ant mimic jumping spider *Myrmarachne* sp.
(family Salticidae)

Crab spider *Tmarus* sp. (family Thomisidae, on plant stems and leaves, cryptic at rest with legs held together & outstretched)

Wasp mimic crab spider *Platythomisus* sp. (Thomisidae, when disturbed holds legs laterally & vibrates them to mimic wings)

Flower crab spider *Thomisus* sp. (Thomisidae, sometimes yellow or pink, note the tiny male, usually found on flowers)

Green crab spider *Diaea* sp. (family Thomisidae, in curled up leaves, male similar colour & size, but with longer legs)

Bark crab spider (family Thomisidae, nocturnal, on tree trunks)

Pea crab spider *Thomisops* sp. (family Thomisidae, in curled up leaf with egg sac)

Female zig-zag spider *Argiope flavipalpis* (Araneidae, note thick bands of silk in web, the exact function of which is unknown)[++]

Male zig-zag spider *Argiope* sp. (family Araneidae, much smaller than female, construct similar, but smaller orb webs)

Spiny orb-web spider *Gasteracantha curvispina* (Araneidae, places small tufts of silk in web, often high up in trees)

Kite spider *Isoxya semiflava* (family Araneidae, smaller than *Gasteracantha*, both species sit at the hub of their orb-web)

Grassland orb-web spider (family Araneidae)

Green orb-web spider *Araneus* sp. (family Araneidae, common in forests)

Garbage line spider *Cyclosa* sp. (Araneidae, uses web decoration for camouflage, flipping sideways when predators approach)

Orb-web spider *Pararaneus* sp. (family Araneidae, juveniles spin a horizontal orb-web, but those of adults are vertical)

Tent-web spider *Cyrtophora citricola* (family Araneidae, hangs suspended below stacked egg sacs in large, permanent web)

Four-jawed spider *Tetragnatha* sp. (family Tetragnathidae, build horizontal webs close to fresh water, males have very large jaws)

Horizontal orb-web spider *Leucauge* sp. (Tetragnathidae, in low vegetation)

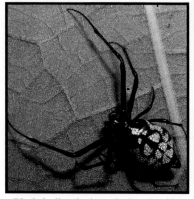

Black & silver horizontal orb-web spider ?*Leucauge* sp. (family Tetragnathidae)

Giant golden orb weaver *Nephila senegalensis* (family Nephilidae, usually in urban areas, legspan the size of a hand!)

Giant forest orb weaver *Nephila fenestrata* (note the tiny male on the abdomen, prefers more shade than the previous species)

Large 'colony' of *Nephila senegalensis* (a common sight on trees or suspended from power cables during the rainy season)[++]

Cluster of *Nephila fenestrata* spiderlings (egg sacs hatch before the rains with adults reaching maturity in about 6 months)

Cobweb spider ?*Theridion* sp. (family Theridiidae, on underside of leaves)

Red cobweb spider *Nesticodes rufipes* (family Theridiidae, common in houses)

Black widow *Latrodectus indistinctus*
(family Theridiidae, abdominal markings
reduced in adults, poisonous to humans)

Brown widow *Latrodectus geometricus*
(Theridiidae, female, characteristic fluffy
egg sacs & male, common in houses)

Dewdrop spider *Argyrodes* sp. (Theridiidae,
kleptoparasites in *Nephila* webs, a single
web may contain many individuals, tiny!)

Giant huntsman *Heteropoda venatoria*
(family Sparassidae, nocturnal, but
sometimes seen in the day, pantropical)

Female green huntsman *Olios* sp.
(family Sparassidae, on plants & in houses)

Male green huntsman *Olios* sp. (longer legs
than female, typical of most spider species)

Burrowing wolf spider ?*Geolycosa* sp.
(family Lycosidae, nocturnal, remains in
deep, silk-lined burrow throughout the day)

Silk-lined wolf spider burrow
(family Lycosidae, animal emerges at night,
burrow may be as much as 1 m deep!)

Small, diurnal coastal wolf spider
?*Pirata* sp. (Lycosidae, with spherical egg
sac attached to abdomen, typical of family)

Large red-jawed wolf spider *Lycosa* sp.
(Lycosidae, bright orange hairs on
chelicerae, nocturnal)

Long-legged wandering spider
(family Ctenidae, at night on bare ground)

Wandering spider (family Ctenidae,
common in forest leaf litter)

Yellow spotted ant-eating spider (family Zodariidae, consuming a large red ant, beneath stones and logs)

Ant mimic spider ?*Apochinomma* sp. (family Corinnidae, first pair of legs held aloft like ant antennae, on vegetation)

White tailed ground spider (family Corinnidae, a large ant ?*Pachycondyla* or mutilid wasp mimic)

Striped ground spider *Copa* sp. (family Corinnidae, very fast, cursorial hunters, usually in leaf litter)

Black ground spider (family Gnaphosidae, nocturnal, shiny with tubular silk organs)

Running crab spider (family Philodromidae, various habitats, small spiders)

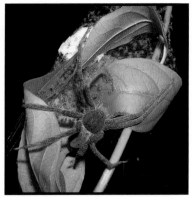

Free living nursery web spider (family Pisauridae, with newly hatched spiderlings in nursery web, charateristic of the family)

Web building nursery web spider *Tetragonophthalma* sp. (Pisauridae, webs common in grass vegetation by mangroves)

Brown lynx spider ?*Oxyopes* sp. (family Oxyopidae, easily identified by their extremely long leg spines)

Green lynx spider *Peucetia* sp. (family Oxyopidae, with egg sac, on green vegetation in exposed sunny areas)

Prowling spider *Cheiracanthium* sp. (family Miturgidae, nocturnal)

Female *Cheiracanthium* sp. with eggs enclosed in silken cocoon within folded leaf

Tube-web spider *Ariadna* sp. (Segestriidae, a spider with only 6 eyes, most have 8, also characteristic is 3rd legs directed forwards)

Tube-web retreat of *Ariadna* sp. (note the characteristic radiating trip-line threads, usually these radiate from a central hole)

Crevice weaving spider *Afrofilistata fradei* (family Filistatidae, sometimes found wandering around in houses, small spider)

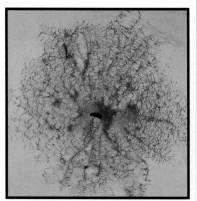

Characteristic messy web & central retreat of Filistatidae (common on outside walls, although the spider itself is seldom seen)

Net-casting spider *Deinopis* sp. (family Deinopidae, nocturnal hunter, huge eyes)

Unused capture net of *Deinopis* (the spider is usually lurking close by waiting for dusk)

Flat crab spider *Selenops* sp. (family Selenopidae, nocturnal, tree trunks & in houses, hides in narrow cracks during day)

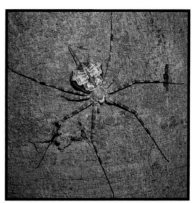

Two-tailed spider *Hersilia caudata* (family Hersiliidae, very common on tree trunks, but extremely difficult to spot)

Velvet spider *Dorceus* sp. (family Eresidae, live in silk-lined burrows in sand, usually in an existing hole, such as ghost crab burrow)

Feather-legged spider *Miagrammopes* sp. (family Uloboridae, weaves a horizontal single-line web between two branches)

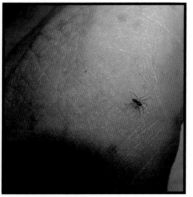

Dwarf spider (Family Linyphiidae, some species build webs, others are free living)

Leaf mesh-web spider (family Dictynidae, note the two pale spiderlings top right)

Star-legged spider *Oecobius pasteuri* (family Oecobiidae, under tiny mesh webs, common on walls, tiny spiders, eat ants)

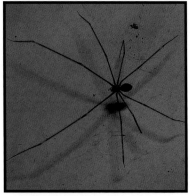

Daddy-long-legs spider *Physocyclus* sp. (Pholcidae, hang from irregular tangle webs inside buildings, vibrate when disturbed)

Long-spinnered red spider *Prodidomus purpureus* (Prodidomidae, free living, nocturnal, little known about behaviour)

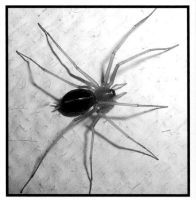

Curly-legged spider *Cithaeron* sp. (family Cithaeronidae, end of legs curl when dead, most often seen in houses, very fast spiders)

Spitting spider *Scytodes* sp. (Scytodidae, in curled up leaves during rainy season)

Palp-footed spider (Palpimanidae, the large first legs are held aloft when alarmed)

OTHER ARACHNIDS

There are several other groups that share a common ancestry with spiders and have similar morphological features, including two main body parts (sometimes fused or segmented), pedipalps (variously modified) and eight legs. Those known to occur in The Gambia are whipscorpions (order Amblypygi), vinegaroons (order Uropygi), hooded tick spiders (order Ricinulei), sun spiders (order Solifugae), laniatores and harvestmen (order Opiliones), ticks and mites (order Acari), scorpions (order Scorpiones) and pseudoscorpions (order Pseudoscorpiones). The last group is not illustrated. They are tiny (usually less than 4 mm) versions of scorpions, but without the tail and live in leaf litter or under bark.

Whipscorpions are flattened animals with very long, antenniforme first legs. They live beneath stones or under loose bark and scurry sideways when disturbed. Occasionally they enter houses, but despite their fearsome appearance are totally harmless. The **vinegaroon** has a long, thin telson (tail-like structure) that releases a spray containing a mixture of acetic acid and a solvent that attacks insect cuticle. Only one species has been recorded from the whole of Africa, with its distribution restricted to tropical West Africa. **Hooded tick spiders** live in the soil of humid forests in West Africa and the Americas, but little is known of their biology. **Sun spiders** (also known as wind spiders because of their great speed) have powerful biting chelicerae (jaws) and a fearsome appearance. They can bite, but are not poisonous. Some species are day active and sometimes they can be seen burrowing into sand.

Laniatores and **harvestmen** are cryptic creatures that prefer dark, humid conditions, such as under rotting vegetation or within tree holes. They feed mainly on living insects, but sometimes also on dead animals or plant juices. **Mites** and **ticks** are an extremely large group of tiny animals and are found globally in all habitat types. Many are parasites of plants or animals and some transmit disease to crops, livestock and humans and are thus of economic importance.

Scorpions have a somewhat unjust, reputation as evil creatures with a fatal sting, which will kill a human in seconds. This is by no means true. Whilst all of them can give a painful sting, most of them are not dangerous to humans, unless you are allergic to them. Nonetheless, they should not be handled and should be given a cautious respect.

Whipscorpion *Damon medius*[++]
(Amblypygi: family Damonidae, first pair of
legs extremely long & sensory, harmless)

Vinegaroon *Etienneus africanus*[+++] (order
Uropygi: family Thelyphonidae, the only
African species, restricted to West Africa)

Hooded tick spider *Ricinoides* sp. (order
Ricinulei: family Ricinoididae, 8 mm, a soil
dweller of humid forests, very cryptic)

Sun spider *Zeria keyserlingi* (order
Solifugae: family Solpugidae, a very fast &
voracious predator found in dry areas)

Laniatore (order Opiliones: family
?Triaenonychidae, beneath rotting logs)

Harvestman (order Opiliones: family
Phalangiidae, found beneath rotting logs)

114

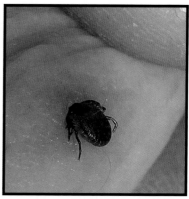

Tick *Amblyomma variegatum* (order Acari: family Ixodidae, an important vector for various diseases of domestic livestock)

Brown dog tick *Rhipicephalus sanguineus* embedded in the skin of the author (order Acari, usually on dogs, rarely bite humans)

Velvet ground mite *Dinothrombium tinctorium* (Acari: Trombidiidae, common, but only for a few weeks after the first rains)

Giant black scorpion *Pandinus gambiensis* (Scorpiones: Scorpionidae, sting painful but not dangerous, found inland, 17 cm long!)

Red-clawed scorpion *Butheoloides* sp.[+] (Buthidae, toxicity of venom unknown)

Fat-tailed scorpion *Buthus occitanus* (Buthidae, under stones, poisonous)

MILLIPEDES & CENTIPEDES

Both **millipedes** (suborder Diplopoda) and **centipedes** (suborder Chilopoda) belong to the order Myriapoda and are characterized by having elongate, segmented bodies with many legs. Most (but not all) millipedes have cylindrical bodies and are slow moving herbivores. They have two pairs of legs on each body segment. They prefer humid conditions, so are usually found in leaf litter or beneath logs and stones. However, during the rainy season they can often be seen foraging in open ground or on tree trunks. Most are capable of discharging offensive smelling secretions, which act as a repellant to potential predators.

Centipedes are dorso-ventrally flattened, have only one pair of legs per body segment and most are very fast. They are found in various habitats, are nocturnal and are predators of other arthropods. The first pair of legs is modified into venomous, biting fangs called maxillipedes. Most centipedes are extremely aggressive and can inflict painful bites that may generate intense pain, swelling and necrosis, and may necessitate medical treatment. However, there are no truly dangerous centipedes and no confirmed fatalities have been recorded. Nonetheless, they should not be handled.

There is barely any non-technical information available on the identification and diversity of West African myriapods. Thus, it is impossible to predict how many species may occur within The Gambia, but all major groups seem to be represented. They are more commonly seen during the rainy season when the humidity allows them to wander around without fear of desiccation.

Rough giant millipede (Diplopoda: family
Spirostreptidae: Trachystreptini)

Smooth giant millipede
(Diplopoda: family Odontopygidae)

Flat rosy millipede (Diplopoda: family Chelodesmidae: ?Prepodesminae, humid forests during the rainy season, 40 mm)

Flat-backed millipede *Sphenodesmus* sp. (Diplopoda: family Gomphodesmidae, in humid habitats during the rains, 60 mm)

Gregarious millipedes (Diplopoda: family Paradoxosomatidae, in humid forests during rainy season, on the ground or tree trunks)

Long-legged centipede *Scutigera* sp. (Chilopoda: Scutigeridae, under logs & stones, also in houses, very fast, 30 mm)

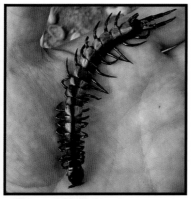

Giant centipede *Scolopendra amazonica* (Chilopoda: family Scolopendridae)

Scolopendra amazonica (banded morph, aggressive & poisonous, various habitats)

BIODIVERSITY & CONSERVATION

This guide illustrates a minute fraction of the biodiversity of The Gambia, and you will certainly see things not included here, and quite possibly that are new to science. Indeed, you may actually be the first person to see the organism in question! For certain groups our biodiversity knowledge of this part of the world is very poor indeed and it warrants further investigation.

There are some serious conservation issues relating to this living museum of natural history, which includes IUCN listed endangered species, such as the western red colobus monkey. Some unique habitats are at risk of disappearing forever due to inadequate perimeter fencing. A prime example of this is Bijilo Forest, a unique primary coastal forest close to the tourist area. In many places the old fence has been breached and well-worn foot trails meander into the forest at several points. This allows non-resident animals such as dogs, goats and cattle to enter, which can cause all sorts of different problems. Much more serious is unauthorized collection of firewood and building materials, which will fragment this already small forest. This is usually done at night by firelight, with such fires sometimes getting out of control, which in theory could devastate much of the forest in a matter of hours during the dry season!

Unfortunately, the Forestry and Wildlife Departments have limited resources and a great deal of land area to protect throughout the country. Any assistance towards the conservation activities of these departments would be greatly appreciated. Please help to protect the magnificent natural heritage of The Gambia for both the Gambian people and their visitors for many generations to come.

Philanthropists should contact the directors of the appropriate departments at:

Department of Forestry, 5 Marina Parade, P.O. Box 504, Banjul, The Gambia

Department of Parks & Wildlife Management, P.O. Box 2164, Serrekunda, The Gambia

ADDITIONAL RESOURCES

Online

www.darwingambia.gm (website of the Gambian Darwin Initiative/Makasutu Wildlife Trust. Contains a useful preliminary checklist of the Gambian flora and fauna (completeness and accuracy highly variable for different groups). As part of this project, Barnett, L., Emms, C., *et al.* produced a series of short (25 pp) general guides on various groups, including common reptiles, amphibians, mammals and butterflies of The Gambia. (Very basic, but with some useful Gambian specific information)

Selected books

Arbonnier, M. 2002. *Arbres, arbustes et lianes des zones sèches d'Afrique de l'Ouest (2nd ed).* CIRAD-MNHN, Paris. (In French, but an excellent field guide with many good colour photos)

Barlow, C., Wacher, T., Disley, T. 1997. *A field guide to birds of The Gambia and Senegal.* Pica press, East Sussex. (The original and most authoritative bird guide for the Senegambia region; there is also a 2005 paperback edition)

Dippenaar-Schoeman, A.S., Jocqué, R. 1997. *African Spiders. An Identification Manual.* Pretoria: Agricultural Research Council. (The best book on African spiders, but more of a technical work, not much use as a field guide)

Filmer, M.R. 1991. *Southern African spiders: an identification guide.* Struik, Cape Town. (A more useful field guide than the above, but less authoritative; covers many groups found in West Africa)

Jones, M. 1994. *Flowering plants of The Gambia.* A.A. Balkema, Rotterdam. (A useful field guide to common plants, but expensive considering it has only 32 pages of photos, covering 160 species, contains additional useful references)

Kasper, P. 1993. *Some common flora of The Gambia.* Stiftung Walderhaltung in Africa, Hamburg. (Out of print, difficult and expensive to obtain, covers additional species not illustrated in Jones' book, but lacks an index and doesn't cross reference photos to text!)

Kingdon, J. 1997. *The Kingdon guide to African mammals.* Academic Press. (An excellent book with distribution maps, showing which species occur in The Gambia)

Larsen, T.B. 2005. *Butterflies of West Africa.* Apollo Books, Stenstrup. (2 large volumes, unwieldy as a field guide and expensive, but beautifully written and a must for anybody interested in Gambian butterflies)

Picker, M., Griffiths, C., Weaving, A. 2004. *Field guide to insects of South Africa.* Struik, Cape Town. (Excellent field guide, including many species that extend to tropical Africa)

Rödel, M.-O. 2000. *Herptofauna of West Africa: volume 1—Amphibians of the West African savanna.* Edition, Chimaira. (Includes all amphibians likely to be found in The Gambia, difficult to obtain)

West African Nature Handbooks series published by Longman: several short (75 pp) publications covering various groups at a basic level, including *West African butterflies and moths* (Boorman, J., 1970), *West African snakes* (Cansdale, G.S., 1961) and *West African lilies and orchids* (Morton, J.K., 1961)

ACKNOWLEDGEMENTS

The author is particularly grateful to the following in The Gambia for their hospitality, advice and discussion: all staff of Bijilo and Abuko Forests and the Department of Forestry, especially Jato Sillah (director of the DoF), Lamin Bojang, Kebba Sonko, Lamin Jammeh and Sulayman Jobe (manager of Bijilo Forest), Alpha Jallow (director of the Department of Parks and Wildlife Management) and Clive Barlow.

The following professional taxonomists are thanked for assistance with provisional identification: Jens Petersen (Denmark), Isabel Rong (South Africa), Nouroudine S. Yorou (Benin) (fungi); Brian Taylor (UK, ants); Connal Eardley (South Africa, Apidae); Donald Quicke (UK, Braconidae); Martin Villet (South Africa, Cicadidae); G.G.E. Scudder (Canada, Lygaeidae); Harry Brailovsky (Mexico, Largidae); Mike Wilson (Wales, Derbidae); Torben B. Larsen and Jon Baker (UK, butterflies); Martin Stiewe (Germany, Mantodea); Jason Londt (South Africa, Asilidae); Andrew Whittington (UK, Platystomatidae, Syrphidae); Max Barclay (UK, beetles); Lukas Sekerka (Czech Republic, Cassidinae); Fabio Cassola (Italy, Cicindelidae); K.D.B. Dijkstra (The Netherlands, Odonata); Wanda Weslowska (Poland), Bernhard Huber (Germany), Dmitri Logunov (UK), Tamas Szuts (Denmark), Matjaz Kuntner (Slovenia), Rudy Jocqué (Belgium) (spiders); Lorenzo Prendini (USA, scorpions); Alan Walker (UK, Acari); Alexander Gromov (Kazakhstan, Solifugae); Luc 'Nouroudine' Paziaud (The Gambia, herptofauna); Dieder van den Spiegel (Belgium), Richard Hoffman (USA), Sergei Golovatch (Russia) (myriapods).

I am extremely grateful to Dmitri Logunov and Phil Rispin (Manchester Museum, UK) for access to, and assistance with, their extensive entomology collection during the preparation of this book. The following are thanked for photographs: Sam Watson* (UK), Natalie James** (UK), Lambert Smith*** (South Africa), Ray Gabriel[+] (UK), Jon Baker[++] (UK/The Gambia), Jeremy Huff & Valerio Vignoli[+++] (Italy). Barry Burke (Manchester, UK) is gratefully acknowledged for his help in designing the cover and for lessons in using various software packages. Dr Roy Armstrong and his students from the University of Cumbria are thanked for their enthusiasm.

Any errors are the responsibility of the author. Dr David Penney is a retired, professional zoologist currently living in The Gambia. He is a Visiting Research Fellow in the School of Earth, Atmospheric and Environmental Sciences at The University of Manchester, UK and an internationally recognized expert on spiders. He can be contacted by email on david.penney@manchester.ac.uk or African.Nephila@hotmail.co.uk and would be grateful to receive any nice Gambian wildlife photographs, particularly of spiders...many thanks!